The Four Lost Men

Old Kentucky Home, the Wolfe boardinghouse.
From left: Ben Wolfe, Fred Wolfe, Thomas Wolfe, unidentified
boarder, Julia Wolfe, unidentified boarder, W. O. Wolfe.
Courtesy of the Thomas Wolfe Collection, Pack Memorial Library, Asheville, N.C.

The Four Lost Men

The Previously Unpublished Long Version

Including the Original Short Story

■

Thomas Wolfe

Edited by Arlyn and Matthew J. Bruccoli

The University of South Carolina Press

Published by the University of South Carolina Press
Columbia, South Carolina 29208

www.sc.edu/uscpress

Manufactured in the United States of America

17 16 15 14 13 12 11 10 09 08   10 9 8 7 6 5 4 3 2 1

Library of Congress Cataloging-in-Publication Data

Wolfe, Thomas, 1900–1938.
    The four lost men : the previously unpublished long version / Thomas Wolfe ; edited by Arlyn and Matthew J. Bruccoli.
        p. cm.
    "Including the original short story."
    Includes bibliographical references and index.
    ISBN 978-1-57003-733-7 (cloth : alk. paper)
    I. Bruccoli, Arlyn. II. Bruccoli, Matthew Joseph, 1931– III. Title.
PS3545.O337F68 2008
813'.52—dc22

                                    2007050121

CONTENTS

ILLUSTRATIONS

ACKNOWLEDGMENTS

Our main obligation is to Susan Halpert, reference librarian, Houghton Library, Harvard University. She provided the microfilms and Xeroxes of Thomas Wolfe's manuscripts and typescripts in the Wisdom Collection. The Houghton is a very well-run rare-books library that serves researchers. Ted Mitchell at the Thomas Wolfe Memorial in Asheville provided crucial evidence about Mr. Helm. Herman Kohlmeyer and Catharine Brosman advised us about New Orleans research facilities. John T. Magill at the Historic New Orleans Collection provided data on local banks. Nicholas Graham, head of public services at the North Carolina Collection, Wilson Library, University of North Carolina at Chapel Hill, is consistently helpful. Dr. Jeremy H. Marshall at the *Oxford English Dictionary* helpfully and promptly answered questions about Wolfe's words. We are grateful to Steven Lynn, who was chairman of the Department of English at the University of South Carolina, for his encouragement. Amber Coker and Judith S. Baughman know what we owe them.

Many readers avoid Thomas Wolfe because he is perceived as a writer for young men. My own experience suggests that if one has not read Thomas Wolfe by sixty-five, then sixty-five is a perfectly good age to begin.

A.B.

INTRODUCTION

Commencing in 1929 the House of Scribner published Thomas Wolfe in untrustworthy texts, which have been perpetuated in uncorrected reprints and inaccurate resettings. Critical editions of his work are necessary, starting with the short stories and long stories. We don't know what or even whom we are reading when we read a Wolfe story now. Francis Skipp's edition of *The Complete Short Stories of Thomas Wolfe* (New York: Scribners, 1987) lacks editorial or textual notes. The editorial history of the published stories is unusually obscure because the textual evidence is incomplete. There is an abundance of manuscript and typescript in the Wisdom Collection at the Houghton Library but almost no proofs of stories.* Wolfe was not a painstaking proofreader—when he bothered with proofs. Moreover, it is probable that the Scribners editors were reluctant to run the risk of having him rewrite his stories in proof.

The familiar criticism of Thomas Wolfe is that he was deficient in sense of form: that his novels and stories are loosely organized or even unstructured and include unnecessary material. The terms "self-indulgent" and "undisciplined" have been freely applied to his published work. This influential charge interferes with the proper evaluation and understanding of his work. At its most pernicious, it provides an alibi for the failure to publish trustworthy Wolfe texts.

Wolfe's short stories and long stories that were published during his lifetime were routinely edited and pruned by somebody else to meet the space requirements of magazines. A twenty-thousand- to thirty-thousand-word Wolfe manuscript would be published in a five-thousand-word

---

*The only marked story galley proof I have seen is for "The Web of Earth"—which is heavily edited in an unidentified nonauthorial hand.

version. Wolfe did not always bother to vet these truncations. The surviving story manuscripts and typescripts permit scholars to recover Wolfe's intentions for these lost works: lost because they were not published as he wrote them. This edition does not provide an "ideal text" of "The Four Lost Men." It is a lightly emended version of the long typescript that Wolfe developed from the short typescript and intended for inclusion in a planned book, never completed, "The Hills Beyond Pentland."

Wolfe's long stories have been misleadingly categorized as novelettes or short novels; such labeling legitimizes criticism of their structure. The long twenty-thousand- to thirty-thousand-word narratives were usually written as pieces of a vast gestating multivolume work and were not intended by Wolfe for separate magazine publication. Sometimes they started as short stories and outgrew the commercial form. Maxwell Perkins salvaged material from Wolfe's stockpile of manuscripts for publication in *Scribner's* magazine—as with "A Portrait of Bascom Hawke" and "The Four Lost Men."

Perkins referred to Wolfe's "dithyrambs"—alluding to the early Greek narrative choral odes for the worship of Dionysus, god of wine and intoxication. This joke makes the point that much of Wolfe's writing is rhetorically expansive—inspired by his excitement with language.

F. Scott Fitzgerald got it right and wrong. He wrote Perkins about *Look Homeward, Angel* in 1930: "John Bishop told me he [Wolfe] needed advice about cutting ect, but after reading this book I thought that was nonsense. He strikes me as a man who should be let alone as to length, if he has to be published in five volumes."[1] Right. But in 1937 Fitzgerald started an argument with Wolfe about "leaver-outers" and "putter-inners" by urging him to emulate "the novel of selected incidents." Wolfe responded to this bad advice:

> . . . your argument is simply based upon one <u>way</u>, upon one method instead of another. And have you ever noticed how often it turns out that what a man is really doing is simply rationalizing his own way of doing something, the way he has to do it, the way given him by his talent and his nature into the only inevitable and right way of doing everything—a sort of classic and eternal art form handed down by Apollo from Olympus without which and beyond which there is nothing?[2]

Wolfe's Story Publications, 1932–1935

There is no record of Wolfe trying to publish stories before 1932. "The Angel on the Porch"—which was not written as a story—was plucked by Perkins from *Look Homeward, Angel* and published in *Scribner's* magazine (August 1929). Wolfe's next story publication, "A Portrait of Bascom Hawke," in the April 1932 *Scribner's*, was not written as a stand-alone story. Perkins removed it from the manuscripts for *Of Time and the River* and entered it in the *Scribner's* short-novel prize contest; it was the cowinner with John Herrmann's "The Long Short Trip." "The Web of Earth" was also published by *Scribner's* in 1932. When Wolfe needed money in 1933, he tried to write sellable magazine stories. Elizabeth Nowell, who became his story agent-editor that year, stated, "Wolfe had no idea of what constituted a salable short story. With the exception of 'The Web of Earth,' his stories had been picked out of his vast mass of manuscript by Perkins, accepted in rough draft by *Scribner's Magazine*, then reworked (and lengthened in the process) by Wolfe, and finally cut and edited by Alfred Dashiell."[3] "The Four Lost Men" did not undergo this prepublication process.

Little is known about Wolfe's working relationship with Dashiell, editor of *Scribner's*. Few pieces of their editorial correspondence survive. But there is an important letter to Dashiell about the magazine text of "The Four Lost Men":

> Dear Fritz: I'm sorry for the delay but here are the proofs of <u>The Four Lost Men</u>—all I've been able to do to it. I've worked all day on it, but I can't make my head work well today—its' worn out and won't work for me—I feel as if I'm taking a big chance with this and have never felt so uncertain about a mss. But I can't do any more now; so will send it on.
>
> I would appreciate it if you or Miss Buckles did this for me: on galley <u>2</u> towards bottom where father says "The first vote I ever cast for President . . . . I cast in 1872 for . . . . . U.S. Grant"—will you please verify all these dates for me? I think I am right about them, but I want the year and the Candidate to be right—in each case the vote should be for the <u>Republican</u> candidate of that year.
>
> Again, Max asked me to cut out references to whores and brothels in reference to Our Presidents, etc. But I notice on galley seven a

direct referent "—did they not carry . . . . . Garfield, Arthur, Harrison and Hayes . . . . . the intolerable burden of their savage hunger into the kept and carnal nakedness of whores"*

If you want to keep this <u>as is</u>, its O.K. with me, but I think you will find that I cut it out of mss. and wrote in a new phrase. If you want to use that, look at mss. again. Please look over such corrections as I have made to see if you approve—if not restore to original. I'm awfully sorry to be so late and not to have done more—I'm tired, but my head is too tired to work for me. <u>Be sure</u> to see that the <u>type-written insertion</u> goes in where indicated on Galley 4—Yours with thanks,

Tom Wolfe[4]

Nowell explains:

> There was also the constant difficulty of too great length: Wolfe
> never wrote a story under the usual limit of five thousand words in
> his entire life, with the exception of brief episodes which were lifted
> virtually untouched from his books, such as "The Sun and the Rain"
> and "The Far and the Near." His stories naturally came out some-
> where between ten and thirty thousand words.[5]

Nowell did not place "The Four Lost Men." She probably began market-ing Wolfe's stories with "Boom Town." That is, making them marketable by cutting and editing them. Twenty-two Wolfe stories were published in magazines during 1932–35. Fourteen were collected in *From Death to Morning*. Perhaps all were excerpted from novels in progress; ten also appear in novels.

Composition and Publication of "The Four Lost Men"

"The Four Lost Men" grew out of Wolfe's research for the character Joe Barrett or Lindau, based on Aline Bernstein's father, actor Joseph Frankau, for *The Good Child's River*. Wolfe consulted the *Encyclopædia Britannica* for background on 1881, the year of her birth, which was the year of President Garfield's murder. Wolfe's pocket notebook for September–December 1931 includes biographical data on Garfield, Arthur, Hayes, and Harrison.

---

*See *Scribner's*, February 1934, 108: "the intolerable burden of all the pain, joy, hope, and savage hunger that a man can suffer, that the world can know?"

This material probably triggered Wolfe's memory of his father's political declamations, which inspired "The Four Lost Men."

Like W. O. Gant, W. O. Wolfe was born in Pennsylvania and claimed a role in the Battle of Gettysburg. He came south in his young manhood. His loyalty to the Republican Party and his denunciation of the Democrats may have been inspired by his sense of being an outsider in the Reconstruction South and by the satisfaction he took in opposing the local Democratic establishment. Hayes, Garfield, and Harrison failed to carry North Carolina.

Garfield, Jas. Abram (1831–1881)

B. Log cabin frontier town, Orange, Cuyahoga County, Ohio.

Walks across country to Cleveland aet. 16—works on lake schooner for canal boatment.

Works way through school as teacher, carpenter, farmer—studies at West. Reserve Eclectic Inst. At Hiram—Goes to Williams—returns to Hiram as principal, enters political life, anti-slavery man—enlists— lt. colonel—then, Brigadier—then maj. Gen'l—gallantry at Shiloh and Chickamauga.

Year 1874—one of trouble—Reconstruction, Credit Mobilier, Salary Grab, Greenback issue.

On July 2, 1881 on way to Wms. College commencement shot in Wash. Rwy. Station by Guiteau.

Arthur, Chester Alan (1830–1886).

B. Fairfield, Vt.—Oct. 5, 1830—son of an Irishman who came to Vt. From Canada.

Enters Union College in 1848 as Soph.—1853 enters law office NY City.

Known as defender of glaring negro cases—1855 gets decision that negroes entitled to ride as whites on st. r'ways.

Quartermaster Gen'l of N.Y. state troops in War—1862 resumes practice—1871 appointed collector of customs for port of NY by Pres. Grant—Office noted for abuse of "spoils systems"—Gen. Arthur makes no reforms.

In 1877 Hayes tries to oust him—In 1878 he is removed—Becomes V. Pres. And Pres. On death of Garfield.

In spite of public fear makes honest pres.—vetoes spoils appropriation of 18 mills. For bigger over little states (1881).

North. Pacific, South. Pac., Asch. Top. And St. Fe completed in his admin.

Wash. Monument—Feb. 21, 1885, dies 1886.

Hayes (1822–1893)

B. In Delaware, Ohio Oct. 4, 1822.

Goes to Harvard Law School practices in Cincinnati—enlists— becomes brig. & maj. Gen'l.

Goes to Congress—in 1868 becomes gov. of Ohio—to 1872. In 1875 again elected. 1876 becomes cand. for pres. Against Tilden. Hayes declared elected 8 to 7 by commission.

Policy of pacification in South—Ends carpetbag govts. Withdraws troops.

Attempts civil service reforms, able and honest.

. . . .

Harrison, Benj. (1833–1901)

B. North Bend near Cincinnati, Ohio—log school house—Miami University—studies law in law office—aet. 21 goes to Indianapolis, soon leading lawyer.

Enlists in Civil War, breveted brig. gen'l.

Then resumes legal profession—elected U.S. Senator 1881— nominated for pres. 1888—defeats Grov. Cleveland.

Passage of McKinley Tariff Bill and Sherman Silver Bill of 1890—

Suppression of Louisiana Lottery—enlargement of navy—civil service reform—arbitration of Bering Sea fur trade with Britain.

Revival of trade—defeated by Cleve. 1892 because of strikes— labor unions against Tariff party.[6]

Hayes, Garfield, Arthur, and Harrison were the four Republican presidents who followed Grant during the Reconstruction and post-Reconstruction periods. (Democrat Grover Cleveland served terms before and after Harrison.) All were Civil War generals—the last ones to serve as presidents. All were self-made men. Garfield was the last president born in a log cabin. Benjamin Harrison was the grandson of President William Henry Harrison, but his family was not affluent. All were Ohio-bred, although Harrison achieved his success in Indiana. All were able presidents whose terms were not marked by egregious scandals—apart from the disputed Hayes-Tilden election. None was a great or distinguished president.

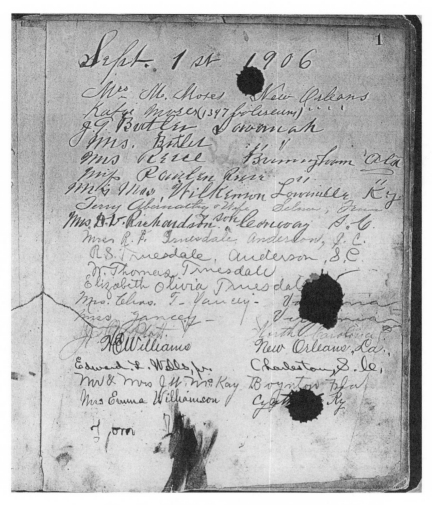

Page from the 1906 Old Kentucky Home guest register,
signed by Mrs. and Mr. Moses—with "Tom W" at bottom.
Courtesy of the Thomas Wolfe Memorial, Asheville, N.C.

Given Wolfe's customary use of character sources in his fiction, it is to
be expected that he drew on actual boarders for Mr. Helm. The Old Kentucky Home guest register for 1907 is signed by Mrs. and Mr. Philip Helm
of New Orleans. Philip Leopold Helm (d. 1938) was a letter carrier. He
had no connection with a New Orleans bank, and it is not known whether
he spoke with a German accent. The guest register for 1906 includes an

entry for "Mrs Mr. Moses New Orleans." In 1906 Elkin Moses was cashier at the Equitable Life Assurance Society in the Hibernia Bank Building. Nothing further is known about his business life. (This register page has the smeared ink signature "Tom W" at the bottom. Wolfe was not yet six years old.) Mr. Helm of "The Four Lost Men" is possibly an amalgam of Philip Helm and Elkin Moses. Or Wolfe may have combined Helm and Moses with an invented character.

The manuscript evidence (see the chapter "The Manuscripts and Typescripts") establishes that Wolfe wrote a short version of "The Four Lost Men." He then enlarged it to twenty-one thousand words; but he used the original, shorter version for the *Scribner's* magazine short story. The setting copy and proofs are not extant. Wolfe acceded to Perkins's request that the reference to the presidents as brothel frequenters be deleted for magazine publication. Consequently, in both *Scribner's* and *From Death to Morning*, they do a great deal of anticipatory waiting outside houses, but the reader is not told what they are waiting for.

Two characters in the long version, Helm and McKeithan, are missing in the magazine and book texts. The previously unpublished version includes the story line for Helm's ruin resulting from the New Orleans bank failure. There is no evidence that Wolfe wrote any of the manuscript material more than once: no rewriting, copying, or cutting on the manuscript pages. Presumably Wolfe developed the long version from the short one, adding material about the boarders and W. O. Gant's death because he intended to incorporate it into "The Hills Beyond Pentland," eventually abandoned. As published in *Scribner's*, "The Four Lost Men" is much as Wolfe originally wrote it. Forty-seven pages (6–35 and most of 37–54) of a total of seventy-two were added to expand the story for the unpublished "Hills Beyond Pentland"; but after page 54, except for bowdlerization (two pages' worth), the addition of one page, and reordering of a few paragraphs, the *Scribner's* story is close to the long typescript.

"The Four Lost Men" typescript has two cover pages. One identifies it as part of "The Hound of Darkness," Wolfe's unfinished saga of nighttime America. "The Hound of Darkness" became the prologue for "The Hills Beyond Pentland," the fictionalized history of Wolfe's mother's people he worked on during 1932–33.* The other cover page alters the title from

---

*This work was not the same as *The Hills Beyond*—the volume of short pieces assembled by Aswell in 1941.

"The War in April" to "The Four Lost Men." Wolfe's 8 February 1934 report on the work accomplished during his Guggenheim Fellowship year describes the 1933 *Scribner's* magazine stories:

> There is one final thing about these pieces and their relation to the book. All of them, with the exception of The Four Lost Men, belong to the first book of a series, that is to the manuscript which Mr. Perkins now has, which will probably be called Time and the River, and which will be published this year. The Four Lost Men belongs to a second book of a series which will be called The Hills Beyond Pentland, of which I now have about 200,000 words in typed manuscript.[7]

When "The Four Lost Men" appeared in the February 1934 *Scribner's*, Wolfe wrote to Robert Raynolds: "I am glad you liked the last piece in *Scribner's*. Perkins liked it, too, and says the time will come when every one will know what it's all about, which seems plain enough to me now, but I think some people may be puzzled by it now."[8]

The stories in *From Death to Morning* were selected by Perkins for publication in *Scribner's* to support Wolfe between *Look Homeward, Angel* and *Of Time and the River*. Publishers were not generous with advances during the Thirties. While Wolfe was in Europe during March through July 1935, Perkins assembled *From Death to Morning* and apparently had it set in galleys. Wolfe, who was brooding about what he regarded as Perkins's high-handed editorial interference with *Of Time and the River*, was concerned that the collection would be published without his final revisions and enjoined Perkins from Colorado on 12 August 1935:

> Finally, you must not put the manuscript of a book of stories in final form until after my return to New York. If that means the book of stories will have to be deferred till next spring, then they will have to be deferred, but I will not consent this time to allow the book to be taken away from me and printed and published [referring to the publication of *Of Time and the River*] until I myself have had time to look at the proofs, and at any rate to talk to you about certain revisions, changes, excisions, or additions that ought to be made. I really mean this, Max.[9]

Some thirteen hundred words were cut from "The Four Lost Men" between *Scribner's* and *From Death to Morning*, all the substantial cuts occurring in the last third of the story. Only a few words were added—which was unusual for Wolfe. (See the chapter "The Four Lost Men: Substantive Variants between Previously Published Versions.")

The timing for production and publication of *From Death to Morning* was very tight. Wolfe was in New York between 4 and 27 July 1935, while he was writing his speech for the Colorado Writers' Conference, published as *The Story of a Novel* in 1936. He returned to New York from the West during the last week of September, when proofs for the story volume were ready. Wolfe's marked *From Death to Morning* galleys do not survive, but he was never a painstaking proofer. He worked on the book proofs with Scribners editor John Hall Wheelock, who had handled the proofing for *Look Homeward, Angel* and *Of Time and the River*. On 18 October, Wheelock reported to Wolfe, "All the proofs of 'From Death to Morning' are in the printer's hands. . . . if there are any corrections you wish to make, they can be made in page proof, which I hope to have to-morrow."[10] Copies of the book were ready by 29 October 1935, the day Wolfe inscribed one for Aline Bernstein.

From Death to Morning, the only collection of Wolfe's stories published during his lifetime, was on sale 14 November 1935. The seventy-five hundred copies of the first printing sold out; it was reprinted in 1935, and copies were remaindered. William Heinemann published a London edition in 1936.[11]

Scribners didn't know how to promote Wolfe's first collection of stories. The prepublication catalogue copy emphasized their humor and revealed that "The Four Lost Men" "is based on a memory." True enough. It is about time and memory: Wolfe's memory, the narrator's memory, his father's memory, and American memory. Referring to the narrator's father, the typescript employs the phrase "sorrow of irrecoverable memory" (this volume, p. 5, ll. 11–12), followed by "sorrowful time and memory" (p. 5, l. 16), "sorrow of time and memory" (p. 10, l. 1), and "sorrowful acceptance of time and memory" (p. 11, ll. 18–19). The jacket flap copy calls attention to "some of the five and six page stories which for economy and precision of style are unsurpassed." The reviews of the collection were unenthusiastic — except for those by Wolfe's friends Hamilton Basso in the *New Republic* ("gains its chief distinction from those pages of dithyrambic declamation")[12] and Clayton Hoagland in the *New York Sun* ("a sustained flight of lyricism").[13] In a mixed *New York Herald Tribune Books* notice that reviewed Wolfe's height as well as his stories, Ferner Nuhn cited "The Four Lost Men" as "most original in conception."[14] Wolfe reacted to Nuhn in the inscription for the copy of *From Death to Morning* he presented to Henry Volkening, a former New York University colleague:

> I'm a little sad as I write you this. I've just read the first review of this book—in next Saturday's Herald-Tribune—which pans it and sees little in it except a man six foot six creating monstrous figures in a world of five feet eight.—I do not think this is true, but now I have a hunch the well known "reaction" has set in against me, and that I will take a pounding in the book.—Well, I am writing you this because I believe that as good writing as I have ever done is in this book—and because my faith has always been that a good thing is indestructible and that if there is good here—as I hope and believe there is—it will somehow survive.—This is a faith I want to have, and that I think we need in life—and that is why I am writing you this— not in defense against attacks I have receive—but just to put this on record *in advance* with you, who are a friend of mine.—So won't you put this away—what I have written—and keep it—and if someday it turns out I am right—won't you take it out and read it to me?
>
> Yours—
Tom[15]

Howard Mumford Jones (the *Saturday Review of Literature*) and R. P. Blackmur (*Southern Review*) denounced the formlessness of the stories. Jones: "violates the simplest principles of construction. 'The Four Lost Men,' for example, begins as a prose rhapsody about a young man in war- time, continues as a realistic transcript of the elder Gant's conversation regarding presidential elections, and concludes as a Wolfian prose-poem about life, death, war, and time."[16] Blackmur: "Form, we might say, is the only sanity—the only principle of balanced response—possible to art."[17]

The London *Times Literary Supplement* unsigned review of the British edition got it right:

> There is, at his best, something of incantation in his descriptive, exhortatory passages, recreating not only sights and smells but a whole emotional attitude to all that he has known and felt in teem- ing, seething American living and in his own being.
>
> No one story in this collection is so characteristic as "The Four Lost Men," in which, recalling his father's words about four figures of the past, he identifies himself with them:—

> *Had they not, as we, then turned their eyes up and seen the huge*
> *starred visage of the night, the immense and lilac darkness of Amer-*
> *ica in April? Had they not heard the sudden, shrill, and piping whis-*
> *tle of a departing engine? Had they not waited, thinking, feeling,*
> *seeing then the immense mysterious continent of night, the wild and*
> *lyric earth, so casual, sweet, and strange familiar, in all its space and*
> *savagery and terror, its mystery and joy, its limitless sweep and rude-*
> *ness, its delicate and savage fecundity? Had they not the visions of*
> *the plains, the mountains, and the rivers flowing in the darkness, the*
> *huge pattern of the everlasting earth and the all-engulfing wilderness*
> *of America?*

Admittedly such writing must either succeed or fail completely. It is either magnificent or nonsense. In our view it is often the one; the depth of feeling behind saves it from ever becoming the other.[18]

Literary crimes are collaborations. The proper recognition of Thomas Wolfe's genius and the correct judgment of his work continue to be impeded by the circumstances of his publication. This statement applies to most of his long or short stories. The blame for the bad published texts of Wolfe adheres to him because he was not a painstaking reviser-polisher and proofer. Indeed, study of his work in progress indicates that Wolfe was more concerned with getting it all down than with publication. But blame attaches to the editors and publishers who did not serve him well. The proofreading standards at 597 Fifth Avenue were relaxed. Probably the task was impossible to perform properly while Wolfe was alive and writing. Since then Wolfe scholars have given scant attention to his texts. Most of his published work—lifetime and posthumous—exists in unreliable or suspicious editions.

M.J.B.

Notes

1. F. Scott Fitzgerald to Maxwell Perkins, 1 September 1930, in Matthew J. Bruccoli with Judith S. Baughman, eds., *The Sons of Maxwell Perkins* (Columbia: University of South Carolina Press, 2004), 120.

2. Ibid., 257.

3. Elizabeth Nowell, *Thomas Wolfe: A Biography* (Garden City, N.Y.: Doubleday, 1960), 233.

4. Wolfe to Alfred Dashiell, late 1933, in Matthew J. Bruccoli and Park Bucker, eds., *To Loot My Life Clean: The Thomas Wolfe–Maxwell Perkins Correspondence* (Columbia: University of South Carolina Press, 2000), 123.

5. Nowell, *Thomas Wolfe*, 233.

6. Richard S. Kennedy and Paschal Reeves, eds., *The Notebooks of Thomas Wolfe* (Chapel Hill: University of North Carolina Press, 1970), 2:563–65.

7. Wolfe to Henry Allen Moe, 8 February 1934, in Bruccoli and Bucker, *To Loot My Life Clean*, 120.

8. Wolfe to Robert Raynolds, 2 February 1934, in Elizabeth Nowell, ed., *The Letters of Thomas Wolfe* (New York: Scribners, 1956), 405.

9. Wolfe to Maxwell Perkins, 12 August 1935, in Bruccoli and Bucker, *To Loot My Life Clean*, 172.

10. Wolfe to John Hall Wheelock, 18 October 1935, in ibid., 184.

11. Carol Johnston, *Thomas Wolfe: A Descriptive Bibliography* (Pittsburgh: University of Pittsburgh Press, 1987), 49–59.

12. Hamilton Basso, review of *From Death to Morning*, by Thomas Wolfe, *New Republic*, 1 January 1936, 232.

13. Clayton Hoagland, review of *From Death to Morning*, by Thomas Wolfe, *New York Sun*, 14 November 1935, 26.

14. Ferner Nuhn, review of *From Death to Morning*, by Thomas Wolfe, *New York Herald Tribune Books*, 17 November 1935, 7.

15. Henry Volkening, "Tom Wolfe: Penance No More," *Virginia Quarterly Review* 15 (Spring 1939): 215. See Arlyn Bruccoli and Matthew J. Bruccoli, eds., *Thomas Wolfe's Friendship with Henry Volkening* ([Akron, Ohio]: Thomas Wolfe Society, 2005).

16. Howard Mumford Jones, review of *From Death to Morning*, by Thomas Wolfe, *Saturday Review of Literature*, 30 November 1935, 13.

17. R. P. Blackmur, review of *From Death to Morning*, by Thomas Wolfe, *Southern Review* 1 (Spring 1936), 897–99.

18. "American Incantation," unsigned review of *From Death to Morning*, by Thomas Wolfe, *Times Literary Supplement*, 21 March 1936, 241.

Editorial Plan /
Emendations Policy

Although manuscript material can be assembled for all but eight of the seventy-two typed pages of the long version of "The Four Lost Men," there is no coherent manuscript draft for any version, short or long. The segments of manuscript demonstrate that Wolfe wrote a short version of the story first; he did not cut a finished long story to make it conform to acceptable magazine length. The expanded story was intended for the never-completed "The Hills Beyond Pentland" (not to be confused with the 1941 posthumous collection of short pieces, *The Hills Beyond*); "The Hills Beyond Pentland" had been abandoned when, in 1935, "The Four Lost Men" (reduced by more than thirteen hundred words from the *Scribner's* magazine story) was published in the collection *From Death to Morning*.

The seventy-two-page typescript (secretarial; Wolfe did not type) that serves as the copy-text for this edition is coherent, though it has short pages that indicate piecing, and complete except for five pages, supplied from other (fragmentary) copies of what must be the same typesetting, the duplicated pages of the fragments being the same as the corresponding pages of the copy-text. The copy-text pages are numbered by hand, almost certainly by Wolfe. There is evidence that Wolfe intended other expansion: boarder Jim Blackshire is named early in the story, along with Helm and McKeithan, but he does not appear again; and although Wolfe wrote an account of Mr. Helm's receiving the telegram announcing the collapse of the bank in New Orleans, he did not succeed in fitting it into the story— he deleted a paragraph in the seventy-two-page typescript that foreshadows it. The paragraph is included here (p. 15) in brackets indicating deletion;

the three typed pages about the telegram and bank failure appear in the chapter "The Bank Failure."

The manuscript segments, pieced together to conform to the copy-text typescript, have been collated for the purpose of checking the typescript readings. The emendation policy is to restore Wolfe's manuscript readings and to correct errors of fact. Spelling errors have been corrected. Substantive emendations of copy-text (including Wolfe's own) are listed and explained in the textual and editorial notes. Unclear or confusing punctuation has been cautiously emended; where meaning is clear, Wolfe's punctuation is not regularized. The comma that precedes "and" where there is a series of nouns or adjectives, for example, was irregularly employed by Wolfe. The editors have regularized only the series "Garfield, Arthur, Harrison and Hayes"—omitting the comma, as Wolfe does thirteen times (against seven inclusions).

"Homer did not grow weary of the siege of Troy. . . . Neither, having looked upon that sea and known its color, was he ashamed to repeat a thousand times that it was 'wine-dark'; nor did any living man grow weary when he told him so." Thus in a paragraph (p. 23) that is part of a thirty-page section of typescript not in the *Scribner's* magazine or *From Death to Morning* versions of "The Four Lost Men," Wolfe's narrator defends his father's love of the familiar phrase and the familiar story. His championship of "the living man who does not stale of life" and his attack on "the living dead . . . who have never known innocence, exultancy or joy" are aimed also at Wolfe's own critics and their complaints of his repetition of anecdote and expression.

Avoidance of repetition was not an editorial consideration in the publication of "The Four Lost Men" in *Scribner's* magazine. The word "lilac," describing evening darkness, appears five times, and "goat-cry" twice; "light, ill-laid, ill-joined rails" appears two paragraphs before "light, racketing, ill-joined little rails"; "the humid, subtly fresh, half-rotten river" is separated by two pages from "the harbor, fresh, half-rotten," which is followed on the next page by "fresh half-rotten harbor smells." Inconsistent attempts to reduce repetition were made in cutting the *Scribner's* magazine story for *From Death to Morning*. "Lilac" appears more than once, but it is also (perhaps coincidentally) cut as part of other, long cuts. The first mention of "light ill-joined rails" is cut, leaving only one. Both "goat-cries" are deleted—curiously, but avoidance of repetition may have been the intention; it was a favorite expression of Wolfe's (used three times in *O Lost*, for example). But all three instances of "fresh, half-rotten" were retained in *From Death to Morning.*

It is likely that, had Wolfe himself prepared the long version of "The Four Lost Men" for publication, some of these—and other—repeated words and phrases would have been deleted. The editors have preferred to follow the examples of Homer and the narrator's father, and we have left them alone. Cuts that Wolfe did make are indicated in brackets.

A.B.

The Four Lost Men

■

The Four Lost Men
Long Version

Suddenly, at the green heart of June, beneath the starred tent of deep-breasted night, I heard my father's voice again. That year I was sixteen, [the week before I had come home from my first year at college,] and the huge thrill and menace of the war, which we had entered just two months before, in April, filled our hearts. And war gives life to men as well as death. It fills the hearts of young men with wild song and jubilation. It wells up in their throats in great-starred night with a savage goat-cry of exultant pain and joy. And it fills them with a wild and wordless prophesy not of death, but life, for it speaks to them of new lands, triumph, and dis-covery, of heroic deeds, the fame and fellowship of heroes, and the love of glorious unknown women – of a shining triumph and a grand success in a heroic world, and of a life more fortunate and happy than they have ever known.

So was it with us all that year. Over the immense and waiting earth, the single pulse and promise of the war impended. One felt it in the little towns at dawn, with all their quiet, casual, utterly familiar acts of life beginning. One felt it in the route-boy deftly flinging the tight-folded block of paper on a porch, a man in shirt-sleeves coming out upon the porch and bending for the paper, the slow-clopping hooves of the milk horse in a quiet street, the bottle-clinking wagon, and the sudden pause, the rapid footsteps of the milkman and the clinking bottles, then clopping hoof and wheel, and morning stillness, the purity of light, and the dew-sweet bird-song rising in the street again.

In all these ancient, ever-new, unchanging, always magic acts of life and light and morning one felt the huge impending presence of the war. And one felt it in the brooding hush of noon, in the warm dusty stir and flutter and the feathery clucking of the sun-warm hens at noon. One felt it in the ring of the ice-tongs in the street, the cool whine of the ice-saws droning through the smoking block. One felt it poignantly, somehow, in the solid lonely liquid leather shuffle of men in shirt-sleeves coming home to lunch in one direction in the brooding hush and time-enchanted spell of noon, and in screens that slammed and sudden silence. And one felt it in the humid warmth and hungry fragrance of the cooking turnip greens, in leaf and blade and flower, in smell of tar, and the sudden haunting green-gold summer absence of a street-car after it had gone.

In all these ancient, most familiar things and acts and colors of our lives, one felt, with an intolerable entrail-numbing ecstacy, the huge impending presence of the war. The war had got in everything: it was in things that moved and in things that were still, in the animate red silence of an old brick wall as well as in all the thronging life and traffic of the streets. It was in the faces of the people passing, and in ten thousand familiar acts and moments of man's daily life and business.

And lonely, wild, and haunting, calling us on forever with the winding of its far-lost horn, it had got into the time-enchanted loneliness of the magic hills around us, in all the sudden, wild and lonely lights that came and passed and vanished on the massed green of the wilderness.

The war was in far cries and broken sounds and cow bells tinkling in the gusting wind, and in the far wild wailing joy and sorrow of a departing train, as it rushed eastward, seaward, war-ward through a valley of the South in the green spell and golden magic of full June. The war was in the ancient red-gold light of fading day, that fell without violence or heat upon the streets of life, the houses where men lived, the brief flame and fire of sheeted window panes.

* * *

And it was in field and gulch and hollow, in the sweet green mountain valleys fading into dusk, and in the hill-flanks reddened with the ancient light, and slanting fast into steep cool shade and lilac silence. It was in the whole earth breathing the last heat and weariness of day out in the huge hush and joy and sorrow of oncoming night.

Finally, the war had got into all sounds and secrecies, the sorrow, longing, and delight, the mystery, hunger, and exultant joy that came from the deep-breasted heart of fragrant, cool, and all-engulfing night. It was in the sweet and secret rustling of the leaves in summer streets, in footsteps coming quiet, slow, and lonely along the darkness of a leafy street, in screen doors slammed, and silence, the distant barking of a dog, far voices,

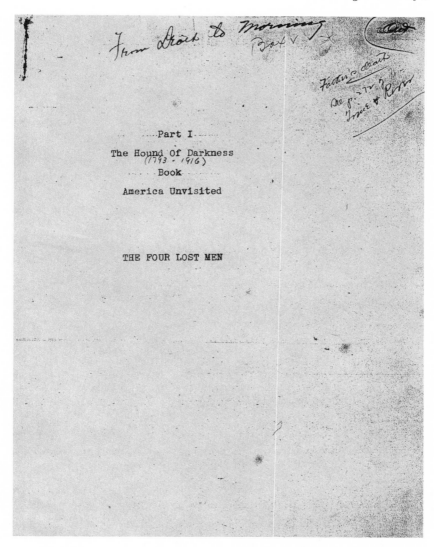

Title page for the projected work that included "The Four Lost Men."
Courtesy of the Wisdom Collection, Houghton Library, Harvard University

laughter, faint pulsing music at a dance, and in all the casual voices of the night, far, strangely near, most intimate and familiar, remote as time, as haunting as the briefness of our days.

And suddenly, as I sat there under all the proud and secret mystery of huge-starred, velvet-breasted night, hearing my father's great voice sounding

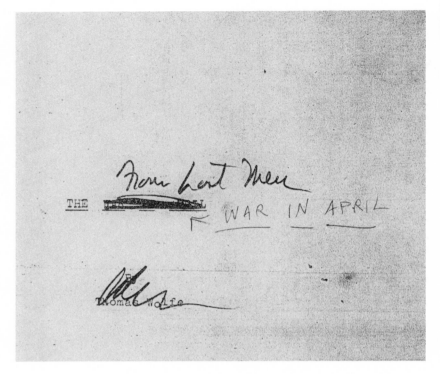

Revised title page. The replacement title is in Wolfe's hand.
Courtesy of the Wisdom Collection, Houghton Library, Harvard University

from the porch, the war, with a wild and intolerable loneliness of ecstasy and desire, came to me in the sudden throbbing of a racing motor far away, silence, an image of the cool sweet darkness of the mountainside, the white flesh and yielding tenderness of women, and even as I thought of this I heard the rich sensual welling of a woman's voice, voluptuous, low and tender, from the darkness of a summer porch across the street.

What had the war changed? What had it done to us? What miracle of transformation had it wrought upon our lives? It had changed nothing; it had heightened, intensified, and made glorious all the ancient and familiar things of life. It had added hope to hope, joy to joy, and life to life; and from that vital wizardry it had rescued all our lives from hopelessness and despair, and made us live again who thought that we were lost.

The war seemed to have collected in a single image of joy, and power, and proud compacted might all of the thousand images of joy and power and all-exulting life which we had always had, and for which we had never had a word before. Over the fields of silent and mysterious night it seemed that we could hear the nation marching, that we could hear, soft and thunderous in the night, the million-footed unison of marching men. And that single glorious image of all-collected joy and unity and might had given new life and new hope to all of us.

My father was old, he was sick with a cancer that flowered and fed forever at his entrails, eating from day to day the gaunt sinew of his life away beyond a hope or remedy, and we knew that he was dying. Yet, under the magic life and hope the war had brought to us, his life seemed to have revived again out of its grief of pain, its death of joy, its sorrow of irrevocable memory.

For a moment he seemed to live again in his full prime. And instantly we were all released from the black horror of death and time that hung above him, from the nightmare terror that had menaced us for years. Instantly we were freed from the evil spell of sorrowful time and memory that had made his living death more horrible than his real one could ever be.

And instantly the good life, the golden and exultant life of childhood, in whose full magic we had been sustained by all the power and richness of his life, and which had seemed so lost and irrecoverable that it had a dream-like strangeness when we thought of it, had under this sudden flare of life and joy and war returned in all its magic and triumphant colors. And for a moment we believed that all would be again for us as it had been, that he never could grow old and die, but that he must live forever, and that the summertime, the orchard and the singing, would be ours, and ours forever, and could never die.

I could hear him talking of old wars and ancient troubles, hurling against the present and its leaders the full indictment of his soaring rhetoric, that howled, rose, fell and swept out into the night, piercing all quarters of the darkness with the naked penetration which his voice had in the old days when he sat talking on his porch in summer darkness, and the neighborhood attended and was still.

Now as my father talked, I could hear the boarders on the porch attending in the same way, the stealthy creak of a rocker now and then, a low word spoken, a question, protest or agreement, and then their hungry, feeding, and attentive silence as my father talked. From time to time some of the boarders, whose politics for the most part differed from my father's,

BLOCK FROM SQUARE   NEWLY FURNISHED
OR POSTOFFICE   THROUGHOUT

Old Kentucky Home

48 Spruce Street   Asheville, N. C.

JUST OFF THE CAR LINE

LARGE LAWNS   NO SICK PEOPLE

RATES REASONABLE

MRS. JULIA E. WOLFE

PHONE 769   PROPRIETRESS

Our Auto Rides You from the Station to the House Free

Business card for the Wolfe boardinghouse.
Collection of the editors

would interrupt him with a laugh of good-natured protest at some partisan extravagance of rhetoric, or with words of some earnest and heated denial. When this happened, as was his custom, he would pay no attention whatever to their arguments. Rather, he would pause, like a caged animal crouched for a spring, lunge forward violently, spit, hitch nervously in his chair, while his cold-grey and unseeing eyes, at once so shallow, un-deep, furious, and lonely, went flickering restlessly about in the boney, deep-sunk, slanting and almost reptilian cage-formation of his skull.

Then, when the words of argument or denial had ceased, he would wet his great thumb briefly, clear his throat savagely, and launch immediately again into the full tide of his invective rhetoric, paying no attention to what had been said to him. All of his life he had been this way. He never paused to argue, he had no interest in the fine points of debate. His interest was in soaring affirmation and whole-hearted curse and, like Dr. Samuel Johnson, if he failed to shoot you with his gun, he would knock you down with the butt of it, and go on heedless of reason or of right.

This now happened. From time to time I would hear the voices of three of the boarders, and my sister's voice, and then my father, breathing furiously and obliviously in these interrupted periods, clearing his throat savagely, and lunging forward in full swing again.

The three boarders who dared to interrupt him were all men, and all had come to my mother's house in summertime for many years. One was an old German from New Orleans named Helm. Another was a genial red-faced man named Jim Blackshire, who was clerk of the court in the South Carolina mill town one hundred miles away where my oldest sister lived. The third, also a South Carolinian, was a man named McKeithan. He was a permanent boarder at my mother's house, and was employed by a jeweller in town as his assistant.

Of all these men we had known old Mr. Helm the best, and felt for him the deepest and most friendly affection. He had been coming to my mother's house since 1907, the summer when she had first acquired the property. Somehow the sight of his broad and kindly face, the sound of his guttural and gentle voice evoked for me the memory of an entire past which I had known and which already seemed lost and colored by the strange golden hue and magic of old time – old time that we ourselves have lived in childhood and that seems, on this account, so strange and wonderful.

Now when I saw and heard old Mr. Helm I would think not only of all the vanished lives of the first boarders, but of all the event, romance, and adventures of their lives, the songs we sang in those first summers and the things we did. The memory of these lives – lives that had come to us from everywhere, that had been drawn in to us on the impulsion of blind chance from a thousand towns and cities, out of the faceless and unknown man-swarms of the earth – had always held for me a magic congruence.

There had been for me in all the casual and accidental interweavings of these lives a sense of purpose and design so ordered and inevitable that now I could only think of these people and the whole integument of event they had created as part of a fixed design, an inevitable purpose in our destiny. And yet they had come to our house by chance, had met by accident, and with the magic instancy and familiarity of life itself, had made a new life there.

There they had hated, loved, been rivals, friends, companions, enemies, had taken sides, divided, joined, created a two-month summer world that had in it all the meanness, malice, envy, spite, and hate, all of the love and tenderness, all of the sorrow, joy, delight, and passion men can know. And all of it, in the time-strange spell and magic of those first golden summers of my life, had seemed to me, a child of seven years, inevitable, eternal. But always at the summer's end they had broken all the magic of that world forever, and departed to take up new lives, new adventures, and new labors of their own. And the destruction of that magic world would always leave me with an unutterable sorrow of loss, the lonely rustle of leaves at night in the trees of waning summer, the receding whistle wailing into darkness at the river's edge, the tolling bell, and for a moment, far and lonely, the pounding of great wheels upon the rail.

Now, from all that vanished world, that buried life, no one returned to waken it but Mr. Helm. And he was old, my father was dying, and the huge impending thrill and menace of the war, the gaunt prophecy of new event, hung over us. Therefore the face of Mr. Helm, the sound of his voice, could now revive the old life poignantly, with an incomparable vividness of memory, but sorrowfully, like something never to be brought back again or captured, like the lost magic, all of the hopes, beliefs, and visions of a child.

The others had long since left us. That company of youth, gayety, beauty and adventure which had come to my mother's house in the first years, which had come out of the deep still mystery of the dark and secret South from a hundred places, of which, somehow, the most magic, languorous, sensuous, and exultant place of all was New Orleans – now came no more. They had vanished, were lost, as strangely, sorrowfully and magically as those enchanted years of "1908," with all their thousand lights and qualities of a lost enchantment – the lost songs, words, events, and casual voices of that time in which they came. Where now?

We did not know, and none could find the reason for their absence, except my mother who sometimes spoke of them regretfully, referring to them as "that class of people" saying:

"We no longer get the class of people that used to come here. They go to hotels now – and then, of course, that's so," she said reflectively. "The automobiles came in and everyone who has a car is out to see the country. The old folks would rather go off somewheres in the mountains where it's quiet and they can rest – and the young folks want to be where there's lots of amusement and something to keep them goin' all the time. Where they used to come and stay two months they put up with you for the night and then they're up and gone next day before you know it. It's become a fly-by-night sort of business, sure enough," she said. "There's no money in it any more. The crowd you get nowadays are clerks or counterjumpers or people who come here on three-day excursions. They're out to get all they can for nothing. They're a far different lot from the class of people that we used to get – oh! doctors, lawyers, business men, the leading folks of the

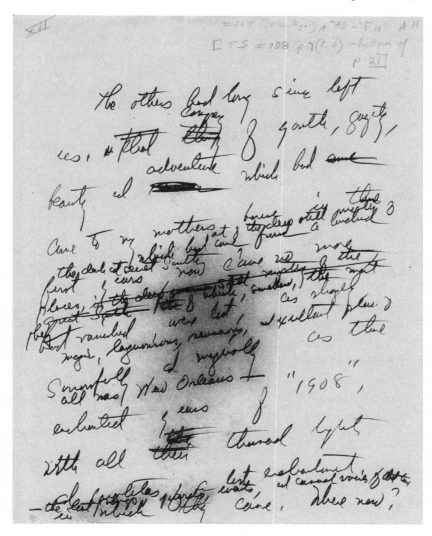

Page from Wolfe's handwritten manuscript.
Courtesy of the Wisdom Collection, Houghton Library, Harvard University

community, good substantial people all of them, would come here with their wives and children – oh! from New Orleans, you know, and every-wheres!" my mother said proudly, and as she said these words, and I saw her high white naked forehead and the child-like innocence in her worn brown eyes, I felt suddenly the rending anguish of intolerable pity that she sometimes roused in me, although why I could not say.

Over all our lives that year there hung a sorrow of time and memory, a feeling, inchoate and unspoken that, whatever the perilous and uncertain future brought to us, golden time of life and hope and full abundant joy had gone from us forever, and could never be recaptured as it was. Even my mother's house had grown shabby, dingy and dilapidated-looking, as if it knew its days of glory had departed.

And now, all through the house – through the wide draughty old halls and in the high calcimined rooms there was an incommunicable but overwhelming feeling of emptiness and departure. And that haunting and sorrowful feeling of sorrow and resignation seemed to have touched, somehow, everyone and everything.

The voices of the boarders on the porch now sounded quiet and sad and lonely in the darkness. And in their comings and goings, even in the way my mother received them, gave them rooms, or watched them as they went away again, there was this strange and terrible sense of emptiness, loneliness, and departure, for which I could not find a word, but which I felt constantly, and knew with a wild and wordless ache of sorrow, mystery, and exultant joy.

It was like the feeling of departed summer, the rustling of leaves in quiet streets at night when summer is over, and lonely footsteps passing in the leafy street, and darkness, a woman's laughter, and the rustling of September leaves again. The boarders themselves were like dry blown leaves. They came and went in the old house with this same feeling of emptiness and sorrow. They were blown past our lives in the old draughty halls and high bare rooms (now naked-bare and rude and shabby as I had never dreamed they were before) with a casual and sorrowful familiarity of affection.

My mother saw them come and go, was kind and tranquil when they spoke to her, and did not trouble much about them. There seemed to be a silent understanding in us all, a quiet fatality of acceptance. We drifted like blown leaves through the wide empty halls of the old house, and went our different ways, and lived most lonely yet familiar to the others in the house.

Sometimes the boarders would pass along the halls, would look in on us as we sat in the kitchen, in the parlour, in the hall, and for a moment the boarders would pause, lean casually against the door and look in on us, talking to us tranquilly and casually with a complete and quiet familiarity of understanding, and then go on again. Sometimes they would ask my mother if anyone had telephoned while they were away, if Jones or Brown or Smith had been there looking for them, and she would answer: "Why, yes, it seems I did see him comin' down the stairs – he went on out – he didn't say what he wanted and I didn't ask," she would tranquilly conclude – "I reckon if he wants to see you he'll be back again."

Or they would ask her casual questions about hot water, laundry, towels, and she would tell them if the water was hot and where to go to get the towels they wanted. And the boarders seemed content with this, and somehow sorrowfully yet affectionately drawn to us all, as if, to be blown like old leaves through the wide draughty halls of the old house, to pass our lives with such a casual, quiet, and intimate affection, to look in on us as we sat in rooms or lay on beds and talked together, to fetch their towels, and ask about the water and the laundry, and then be blown lonely on through the old and sorrowful emptiness of the house again, to come and go, each in his own way as he wanted – was something they desired in life more than order, comfort, care, and service, and with which they were content.

How had we changed? What had time done to us? What was this sorrowful acceptance of time and memory that now hung above our lives forever and that had so transformed us, and haunted even the halls and rooms of the old house with this feeling of emptiness, sadness, and departure? That lost world of those first years of magic – that golden world of "1908" with its integument of a warm, flashing, constantly various and thrilling life – a life of gayety, youth, and summer magic, drawn from a hundred accidental sources, but so intimate, rich, and wonderful that it seemed to me to have the inevitable unity, purpose and design of a densely woven web of destiny, now seemed more lost and strange to me than a vanished dream.

Rather, this world of blown leaves and departure we now lived in had grown dreamlike in its haunting and phantasmal reality until it seemed this old and sorrowful house of haunting vacancy – this house that was so ghostly strange in its stark bare and incredible reality could never have lived and flourished with that great cargo of the past, and was itself the ghostly relic of a reality that had gone forever.

[The feeling that the house gave me was the feeling a man might have when he walks past an old dilapidated house in the great city where he once lived when he was twenty-five, and had come for the first time to live in the unceasing, million-footed city. Then he sees again the room he lived in, with a woman that he loved, and he sees the window that was theirs from which they looked out a thousand times upon the people passing in the street, and he now sees the faces of the people passing in the street about him with a sense of horror, anguish, disbelief, and all of the life that he has lived seems stranger than a dream.

For he knows that in that room were packed incredibly all of the hope, hunger, joy and savage passion youth can know, and that a room can hold. And he sees now that the room was just a room, the house a house, the street a street, and then goes on again, filled with all the mystery, sorrow and the wild regret of time, dark time, that flows forever like a river, and is more real than morning, stranger than a dream, and that haunts us with the briefness of our days. This was the feeling that my mother's house now gave to me.]

This feeling in our lives had come from two main sources. It had come first because the war, which impended now with its terrific thrill and menace, and which had got, passionately and incommunicably, into the most casual and familiar acts of life, and into everything we did and felt and thought, had engulfed us with its tremendous image of central all-embracing reality. The war had overwhelmed our lives and drawn our souls out through our mouths even as the terrific locomotive overwhelms and draws out the souls of people standing on the platform of a little station as it sweeps by them.

For this reason, therefore, not only the lives we had lived, the people we had known, the time, the things, and the events which had long since vanished seemed ghost-strange, magically unreal to us, but even the people around us, the most familiar scenes and acts of all our lives had a dream-like and sorrowful unreality. The familiar world and all the acts and memories of life had now become dream-strange as painted smoke before this overwhelming image of the war which impended, which pounded in our veins like wine, which filled our entrails with the exultant menaces of its dark and secret prophecies, and which called us forth forever to its tremendous life of triumph, glory, new lands, and the love of glorious women.

The second reason for these powerful and incommunicable feelings of sorrow, absence and departure, and the dream-like strangeness of the times we had known, the lives we had led, lay in the constant threat and menace of my father's death. He lived among us now like his own ghost, a memory, a shadow, and a phantom of his own world. Yet, sometimes by a word, a gesture, a living flash of the old fire and power, he would seem to live again in his full prime, as now, as he sat talking of old wars and of lost men to the silent and attentive boarders on the porch.

And when this happened, he could instantly evoke in all its hues of triumph and enchantment not only the lost world of those first years of magic in my mother's house but also the great world of abundance, power, and savage joy, of terror, shame, and rich exultant living which had then been his. That was the world which he had shaped, created, and imposed upon us all, and now, under this phantasmal sorrow of his sunken, waning life, under this dreadful menace of his death that hung above him by a thread forever constricting our hearts with the cold and poisonous fear of an antagonist who always threatened, and who never came, that world of life and joy and magic now seemed lost and sorrowful as dreams, buried forever in a sea-depth of phantasmal time.

What was that world that we had lost? What was that magic life that was so near to all of us, so intolerably near that it was stranger, farther than Hesperides, so near it seemed almost that all we had to do was say a word, or make a spell, or make a little turning of our arm in space to touch it with our hand again, to enter the lost province of its Eden-glories, to make it live again in all its flashing panoply of movement, pulsing warmth, enchanted color, and exultant joy?

[It was the world of the first summers in my mother's house, the summer singing and my father's prime. It was the world of the vanished faces, mystery, the soft low tender laughter of the summer women welling richly from the summer dark, and it was the world of dew-sweet morning with the apple blossoms floating to the ground.] It was the world of the smell of the tar out in the streets at noon, the green-gold aching joy and magic of the dandelions. And it was the world of the spell and wait of drowsy noon, and the time-strange magic of the golden summer.

It was the world where life did not pass in a measured agony of hours and days, and weeks, in grisly endurances of a weary and interminable heat. It was a summer world where life passed magically in one swarming iridescent web of green and gold and velvet night, in a single spell and magic of enchanted time.

It was the world of the vanished faces, the exultant mystery of great-starred, cool-enfolding night, the lilac dark, a woman's laughter, and the rustling of a leaf. And it was the world where we heard great wheels pounding at the river's edge in darkness, the tolling of a bell, the whistle wailing far and lonely through the cool sweet mountain valleys of the South at night, and had no thought of sorrow and departure when we heard those sounds, but rather felt a swelling joy and mystery in our hearts, and thought: "Out of the South, the deep dark South, the ever-still, unmoving, ancient and seductive South, South of the tropic depths, the still reptilian secrecies, the tideless sensual rivers, South of the unknown flowers, the strange perfumes of death and love, the silent trees, the hid desire, the low sweet tender voices and the white flesh of magnolia women – oh, who comes, who comes, who comes to us tomorrow from your dark and secret heart, great South?"

It was the world of the voices singing in the summer darkness, the mellow thrum of violins, the thumped piano and the songs they sang. It was the world of "The Chocolate Soldier," "Tammany," "Has Anybody Here Seen Kelly?" and of "Love Me and the World Is Mine." It was the world of the lovely girls, the beautiful and seductive women coming to us from a hundred places, world of the merry, sensuous, pleasure-loving, and free-handed people of the deep and sensuous South, world of summer-magic, time-enchantment, "New Orleans."

*   *   *   *

And now, of all that world, old Mr. Helm alone was left. From all that life of vanished magic he alone returned, year after year, to revive that lost life in our minds with all the haunting sorrow of its loss. And of us all, old Mr. Helm was the only one who did not know that world had gone forever. He was the only one who did not see how sorrowfully with death my father's life was changed, the ghostly world in which it now lay sunken, nor feel the huge impending menace of the war, a new life, and a transformed world, that hung above us darkly with its secret and unspoken prophecies of triumph and departure, joy and glory, and love and death that was in us, with us, all about us, and had come before we knew it, and was there.

Rather, with the kindly, stolid, unreflecting faith of all his kind, he could not see that anything on earth had changed a bit. My father, whom he worshipped, was still the grandest man on earth to him, his heart the truest, his mind the keenest, the wildest and most extravagant oaths of his vituperative rhetoric, the pure ore of a balanced judgment and a flawless reason, not for a moment to be subjected to the sacrilege of argument or denial. And that my father was an old and dying man, only sick of his life and waiting in the darkness till death came, the enfeebled shadow of his former self, old Mr. Helm did not understand at all.

Likewise, my mother's house had not grown old and shabby, and full of a haunting and sorrowful emptiness to Mr. Helm. Nor could he see that the boarders, too, had changed from that first company of life and youth and ever-pulsing movement, and were only sorrowful poor leaves of boarders now, who came and went in silence, were blown casual and lonely through our empty halls.

No, my mother's house and all the people in it were just the same as they had always been, and nothing in the world had changed at all. Toward all life, and particularly towards his own life, old Mr. Helm felt nothing but the most benevolent satisfaction and assurance that everything had been arranged just as it ought to be. And for that reason, the memory of that good old man as he was that final fatal summer was to haunt my heart forever, and to pierce me with a feeling of anguish, pity, and unutterable regret for all men living when I thought of him.

[For even at that moment as the old man sat there in the summer darkness, worshipfully listening to my father's voice again, solemnly wagging his ponderous and benevolent old head in pious affirmation of everything my father said, his life was ruined, lost, and broken, and he did not know it.]

A German by birth, Mr. Helm had come to America in his sixteenth year, a fugitive, like many others, from the tyranny of the Prussian military system that would have swallowed him. And although he had now lived for more than fifty years in his adopted country, he had never learned to speak its language save in a guttural, almost broken, accent.

For more than forty years old Mr. Helm had been employed by a great bank in New Orleans, and for over thirty years he had been its chief cashier. This bank had been the central passion and consuming loyalty of the old man's life. Of its chief officials – the President, the Vice-Presidents – and its great depositors he spoke with hushed awe, quoting their words and judgments with a reverential deference as great as he accorded the opinions of my father. And for the bank itself he felt a holy devotion that was as sincere and deep as any good priest ever felt for the spiritual divinity of the church.

Year after year the old man had come back to us, bringing his kind old wide-hipped wife along with him, and she would sit there with her hands

folded on her ample stomach, beaming her pride and approval of everything he said from every corner of her good broad face, as the old fellow
smoked his good cigar and told us of his bank.

He boasted of its wealth, the huge amount of its deposits, its invincible
strength and unassailable integrity and the boundless faith and confi-
dence which the public had in it. When he spoke of the bank, it was with
such love and tenderness and utter humility of pride as a man might feel
for a beautiful and beloved son, or as a son might feel for a parent who can
do no wrong.

Then he would boast of the goodness, honor and unbounded kindness
of the chief directors of the bank, and of the princely generosity they had
so often lavished on him.

"Always ven I vent avay on my vacation," he would begin slowly, wagging his big head in slow nods of ponderous affirmation, "*He*" – no need
to name that mighty "*He*," for the solemn look, hushed tone, and reverent
devotion with which the word was spoken told plainly that old Helm was
speaking of the President – "*He* vould call me in to de office und gif to me
a box of fine cigars – ja! I smoke vun of dem now!" the old man cried,
proudly lifting the long Havana in his pudgy fingers and putting it into his
mouth with a somewhat clumsy gesture but with a look of indescribable
satisfaction.

"He vould say, 'Fritz, I make to you a leetle bresent.' Und den he vould
gif me a whole box of dem – ja! De same kind dat he smokes himself!"
the old man said proudly, while his old wife wagged her head in solemn
confirmation of this bounty.

"Den I vould tank him for his bresent und start to go," said old man
Helm, "und he vould alvays sdop me going out de door. He vould say,
'Fritz, vait a minute! Here iss sometink dat I forgot to gif you.' Und he
vould hand to me an envelope mit sometink written on it – alvays de same
ting. Vat you tink it say, eh?" said Mr. Helm, beaming slowly around at
everyone in a gesture of all-inclusive satisfaction. " 'To Fritz Helm – in
token of hiss loyal und valued services to de bank, mit all good vishes for
a happy und successful vacation – Mit de compliments of de directors' –
a check! Ja!" he would cry excitedly. "A check for ein hundert dollars!" he
would shout. "Ein hundert dollars!" he now fairly yelled. "Nod my salary!
Nod my chob! Nein! Nein! Nein!" he would cry angrily, as if someone had
contradicted him. "A gift! Dey gif it to me! Do you see?" – and the old man
would glare wildly at his listeners. "I do nodding for it! Dey gif it to me

every year ven I come away – to – 'To Fritz,'" – and suddenly the old fellow's eyes had grown blind with tears, and his voice became so husky as to be almost inaudible – " 'To Fritz – from de directors,'" he muttered, and suddenly he wiped his old hand with a rough shamed movement across his eyes, and in a moment went on in a quieter tone, "I try to say sometink – to sbeak to him – to make my tanks fer vat dey do – but I gan not sbeak!" and now his voice was old and husky and his eyes had grown blind with tears again. "It all comes svelling here," he whispered, and put his hand upon this throat. "I try to sbeak – but I gan zay nodding – it vill not come! Den," – with a shamefaced smile – "he see I act like a big baby – he make a choak mit me to make me laugh – ja!" he cried, suddenly beginning to chuckle. "He say – 'Now, Fritz, ven you get up dere vere ve gan't look after you – I vant you to look out for de merry summer vidows! Dey're on de look out for younk fellers like you, und I vant you to vatch out fer dem – ja!" said old man Helm chuckling. "He alvays say sometink like dat ven I go avay! . . . Dat vas a choak!" he dutifully explained.

Then his wife would beam round at everyone, nodding her head slowly in a smile of expansive satisfaction which seemed to say, "Ja. Dot vas a choke – und now you gan all laugh aboud it!"

And my father, who had been leaning forward during the whole recital with a faint grin fixed at the corners of his thin pale lips and with his head cocked slightly to the side in an attitude of almost ravenous attentiveness, so that his enormous leathery-looking ear, from which a big tuft of coarse grey hair was growing, seemed almost to sprout outward from his head and seize the words as fast as they came from Mr. Helm's mouth, would now look around at us all with a swift glance of his uneasily restless cold-grey eyes, grin thinly, wet his great thumb briefly on his mouth, spit, and then lunge backward in his chair with a grin of satisfaction, a slow, somewhat rusty chuckle, and a sound which it would be impossible to define exactly but which sounded somewhat like "E'God!"

Although my father had heard this story at least a hundred times, he always listened to it with the same hungry and unwearied interest, bent forward gauntly, head cocked in an attitude of fixed alertness and with his terrific hands hinged in their great-boned clasp upon his knees.

Later, I could not forget my father's hands. They were the largest, most powerful, and, somehow, the most shapely hands I had ever seen. And even though his great right hand had been so crippled and stiffened by an attack of inflammatory rheumatism ten years before that he had never

W. O. Wolfe.
*Courtesy of the North Carolina
Collection, University of North
Carolina Library at Chapel Hill*

regained the full use of it, and since that time could only hold the great
wooden mallet that the stonecutters use in a painful and clumsy half-clasp
between the thumb and the big stiffened fingers, his hands had never lost
their character of life, strength and powerful shapeliness.

The hands gave to the interminable protraction of his living death a
kind of concrete horror that it otherwise would not have had. For as his
powerful gaunt figure waned and wasted under the ravages of the cancer
that was consuming him until he had become only the enfeebled shadow
of his former self, his gaunt hands, on which there was so little which
death could consume, lost none of their former rock-like heaviness,
strength and shapely power. Thus, even when the giant figure of the man
had become nothing but a spectral remnant of itself, sunk in a sorrow of
time, awaiting death, those great still-living hands of power and strength
hung incredibly, horribly from the spectral form of death to which they
were attached.

And for this reason those powerful hands of life evoked, as nothing else
could have done, in an instant searing flash of memory and recognition

the lost world of my father's life of manual power, hunger, fury, savage abundance and wild joy, the whole enchanted structure of the lost life of magic he had made for us. Constantly, those great hands of life joined with an almost grotesque incongruity to that scarecrow form of wasting death would awake for us, as nothing else on earth could do, all of the sorrowful ghosts of time, the dream-like spell and terror of the years between, the years of phantom death, the horror of unreality, strangeness, disbelief, and memory, that haunted us.

So would it be even in death with my father's hands. In their powerful, gaunt and shapely clasp, as he lay dead in his coffin, there would be held and gathered, somehow, all of his life that could never die – a living image of the essential quality of his whole life with its fury and unrest, desire and hunger, its tremendous sweep and relish of its enormous appetites and the huge endowment of its physical and sensual powers.

Therefore, even in his death, as he lay there in his coffin, there was a triumph over death in his great hands. For, curiously, there is usually in the obscene ritual of Christian burial a kind of mercy of obliteration. Under the strong drug of an unnatural and disgusting curiosity, the naked grief and horror of man's death is for the moment dulled. The brutal memory that we want to forget, the intolerable physical horror of a brother's death as he strangles to death before one's eyes in the ropy congestion of his own secretions, writhing on the bed like something impaled upon a hook, and making us writhe forever after in the same way as we try to put it from our minds, seems stranger than a dream when the embalmers have transfigured him with the delicate nuances of their art.

Similarly, the memory of one's father dying in a lake of blood, the great red blot forever spreading on the sheet, the soaking bloody sheet removed and replaced with a white one, the white one red at once with that instant spreading, soaking blot of red again – even the naked mutilation of that memory grows dull when we see him stretched out in a coffin.

The first horror of the knowledge that death in its most loathsome forms can come to a loved familiar figure as readily as to the nameless man-swarm cipher that we do not know, is almost forgotten. Even the rending anguish of hatred, horror, pity, and wet naked shame that one feels at such a time towards one's own family, the wet eyes and oily faces of the women, the hoarse, ugly, and hysterical sobbings, the lack of anything clean, hard, lonely, gaunt and silent in the whole horrible mess and shame and confusion of that blood-soaked death – the literal, physical, and unescapable reality of this horror of death is somehow mercifully drugged by the obscene unrealities of burial.

Now the corpse is stretched out on the splendid satin cushions of the expensive coffin. It has been barbered, powdered, disembowelled, and pumped full of embalming fluid. And as it lies there with its waxen head set forward in its curious gaunt projectiveness, the pale lips firmly closed and with a little line of waxen mucous in the lips, the women come forward with their oily swollen faces, and a look of ravenous eagerness in their eyes, look at it hard and long, lift their sodden handkerchiefs slowly to their oily mouths, and are borne away sobbing hysterically by their equally oily, ravenous sister orgiasts in sorrow.

Meanwhile your father's friends, the stonecutters, masons, building contractors, butchers, businessmen, and the male relatives stand awkwardly about, dressed in their good black clothes, which they seem not to wear so much as to inhabit with a kind of unrestful itchiness, lowering their eyes gravely and regretfully as the women put on their revolting show, talking together in low voices, and wondering when it will all be over.

These circumstances, together with the heavy unnatural languour of the funeral smells, the sweet-sick heaviness of the carnations, the funeral weepy blacks in which the women have arrayed themselves, the satiny sandalwood scent that comes from the splendid coffin, and the fragrant faintly acrid odor of embalmed flesh, particularly when blended with the smell of cooking turnip greens, roast pork and apple sauce out of the kitchen, combine to create an atmosphere somewhat like a dinner party in a comfortably furnished morgue.

In all this obscene pomp of burial there is something so grotesque, unnatural, disgusting, and remote from all we can remember of the dead man's life and personality that everything about him – even the physical horror of his bloody death, now seems so far away we can hardly believe it ever happened. Therefore, we stare at this waxen and eviscerated relic in the coffin with a sense of weird disbelief, unable to relate it to the living man who bled great lakes of blood the night before.

Yet, even in his death, my father's hands still seemed to live, and would not die. And this was the reason why the memory of these hands haunted me then and would haunt me forever after, when he was dead. This was the reason why, when I would try to remember how he looked when dead, I could remember nothing clearly except the powerful sculptured weight and symmetry of his tremendous hands as they lay folded on his body in the coffin. The great hands had a stony, sculptured, and yet living strength and vitality as if Michaelangelo had carved them. They seemed to rest there upon the groomed, bereft and vacant horror of the corpse with a kind of terrible reality as if there really is, in death, some energy of life that will not die, some element of man's life that must persist and that resumes into a single feature of his life the core and essence of his character.

Thus, one could suppose that on the face of a dead poet there might remain – how, where, or in what way we could not tell, a kind of flame, a light, a glory – the magic and still-living chrism of his genius. And on the face of the dead conqueror we might see still living, arrogant, and proud with all its dark authorities the frown of power, the inflexible tyranny of stern command, the spacial infinitude of the invincible will that would not die with life, and that, incredibly, remains, still dark and living in its scorn and mockery of death.

Then, on the face of an old dead prophet or philosopher there would live and would not die the immortality of proud, dark, lonely Thought. We could not say just where that spirit rested. Sometimes it would seem to rest upon the temples of the grand and lonely head. Sometimes we would think it was a kind of darkness in the shadows of the closed and sunken eyes, sometimes the marsh fire of a dark and lambent flame that hovered round the face, that never could be fixed, but that we always knew was there.

And just as poet, prophet, priest, and conqueror each might retain in death some living and fitting image of his whole life's truth, so would the strength, the skill, all of the hope, hunger, fury, and unrest that had lashed and driven on through life the gaunt figure of a stonecutter be marvellously preserved in the granite power and symmetry of those undying hands.

Moreover, in the unwearied and even ravenous interest with which my father heard every repetition of old Mr. Helm's account of the greatness of his bank, and the generosity and benevolence of the officials who directed it, there was evident all of the savage hunger, interest, and delight of a man who loves life dearly, and holds to it fiercely with a bitter hug.

It was the same with everything my father did. Everything that he had found good in life gained and flourished in repeating. His powerful relish for all the joyful, adventurous, warlike, savage, strange and fiercely living acts and histories of life was as strong and sharp as his appetite for food and drink. He could no more have grown tired of a story which had once delighted and interested him than he could have discarded his favorite dishes on the ground that he had been familiar with them since his boyhood, and had now, accordingly, grown weary of them. The reason for discarding one would have seemed as absurd and foolish as the reason for discarding the other.

It will be found that this is true of all men who have loved life fiercely, had the richest and most interesting lives, and have enjoyed life best. For it is only the living man who does not stale of life and its familiar uses; it is always the sterile man who turns life dead. The complaint of tedium, the sneering charge of dulness, the charge of weariness with what was once found good, but now has grown stale through repetition, is the lament of people who themselves were born tedious, weary, stale and dull as hell out of their mothers' wombs.

These are the living dead of life and their dismal legions swarm across the earth, and spread the grey infection of their hopeless taint at all the living roots of joy. Their eyes are lustreless and old, their veins flow slowly with a pale and viscous liquid like embalming fluid, and they have never known innocence, exultancy or joy.

For them all living things on earth turn to a substance of grey ashes in the mouth, and nothing can be done to help them. For them, there is no joy, no hunger, and no savor on the earth. Surfeited from the cradle, jaded even in the loins that wearily begot them, they hate their lives and every living thing on earth with the hatred of their death and impotence.

Nothing is theirs, therefore, but style and newness turning old the moment that they touch it. If they are poor they swarm greyly, wearily along the obscene avenues of night where lights are, seeking constantly about with dead hard eyes and the harsh clamour of their sterile, strident and exacerbated tongues. And if they are rich they sauce up their funeral meats in a quaint and curious realm of pederasts, lesbians, prizefighters, Negro barytones, bicycle riders, jolly old opium eaters and precious kept and sensitively refined young men from the yearning nuances of the art-theatre.

At length, no doubt, this precious and most weary crew submits to the superfetation of death, and the finial anachronism of embalming, and are motored to swift burials and at once forgot.

The living man, however, is never weary of an ancient joy, nor does he sneer at an old magic because he once has known it. Rather, he seeks out constantly the plain, priceless, and uncostly glory of the earth, and knows that there is nothing better. In all his fury, hunger, and unrest, his voyages to strange lands, his constant searching through the streets of life, there is forever the thought of return, the hope of discovery. In such a man there burns forever the belief that all will be again for him as it was once, and that the whole earth will again come instantly to life for him in all the hues of its familiar joy and magic.

The Greeks, one of the more loving, wise, and joyful peoples of the earth, recognized the truth of this with, "Dis a tris tah kala" (The good things are worth trying two or three times). But the man who loves life knows that they could have added: "And if you are a living man and find them good you will not weary of them if you try them twenty thousand times."

Homer did not grow weary of the siege of Troy and of the heroes of that war, although he must have heard the story told by many men. Neither, having looked upon that sea and known its color, was he ashamed to repeat a thousand times that it was "wine-dark"; nor did any living man grow weary when he told him so.

So was it with my father. Just as I had heard him tell a thousand times of old wars and battles and the thousand scenes and stories of a past which he had known and lived, just as I had heard him speak, as now, a thousand times, of the strange lost moments of dark time, of vanished faces, of lost men, of "Garfield, Arthur, Harrison and Hayes," so had I never grown weary of these stories, nor of the way in which he told them, the soaring rhetoric and the familiar epithet, the design that grew, enlarged, and enriched itself forever, but was woven from the old familiar thread of joy.

For my father with his fierce exultant love of life could make the lost world and the buried life that he had known live for me as no one else on earth could do. And because my father had this power and love of life in him, his delight in hearing such stories as old Mr. Helm told to him about his bank was insatiable. So far from ever growing tired of them, he derived constantly a deeper and greater satisfaction from each telling, looking around at all of us with a kind of triumphant satisfaction as he heard the familiar words, as if to say, "You see? What did I tell you?" – even when he had heard the story told unnumbered times – holding his great leathery ear cocked to one side, as he bent forward in an attitude of ravenous attention, and when the story had been told, looking around at all of us with a thin grin of satisfaction, and a slow hoarse almost unwilling chuckle, as he spat strongly, lunged back violently in his chair, wet his great thumb briefly on his tongue, and made an indefinable noise in his throat that sounded like "E' God!"

So had it always been. Now, at the beginning of this first summer of the war, old Mr. Helm had come back again, and now there were new marvels to be added to that old familiar tale. For this year, just the month before, in fact, Mr. Helm, having reached his seventieth birthday and having completed more than forty years of service to his beloved bank, had given in his resignation and prepared to retire to the old age of modest comfort which his savings would enable him to enjoy.

Then, what a leave-taking there had been! What a triumph of farewell and felicitation, joy and sorrow, happiness and regret! On the occasion of his seventieth birthday, which was also the day the old man's resignation took effect, the officials of the bank had given such a banquet in his honor as had never been known before even in the annals of that glorious institution. Not only all the great officials of the bank were there, and the whole personnel down to the last remotest teller, but the most prominent people in the city's life had been invited, and were there in all their stiff white-shirted glory.

The mayor had made a speech of eloquent congratulation, the cashier who was succeeding Mr. Helm had spoken on behalf of employes, and had told of the position of esteem and affection the old man had won in the hearts of all who had known him and worked with him. Finally, "he," the great man himself, seated at the right hand of the guest of honor, had got up and paid such a tribute to the qualities of his departing servant as no one there had ever heard before. The president had spoken with a simple depth and earnestness of feeling of the "bank's great loss," of the place left vacant "in our hearts which no one else can ever fill," and of the honor and respect in which the old man was held by all who had known him "and come to love him as we do." When he had finished, there was not a dry eye left among them, and the old man himself had been so overcome that he was unable to respond.

"It vas not like a sbeech," said old man Helm. "He dit not stand beseit me – he come und stand behind me – he talk to me chust like I talk to you – he call me 'Fritz' – he put his hants upon my shoulters vile he talked like dis – so!" he said, unsteadily stretching his hands before him for a moment – "He say, 'Fritz: no matter vere you go – no matter vat you do – I vant you to know dat our hearts go mit you. . . . Some of us,' he say, 'who vere younk men ven you first came to de bank are now grey-haired mit grand-chiltren of our own. . . . Some of us dat you see here aroundt you to-night vere not efen born ven you first came here. But younk or olt, our hearts are mit you to a man – you haf been more dan an associate, more dan an employe, more dan some-vun ve haf vorked mit und learnt to honor und respect – You haf been more like de fader of our family – a brudder und a friendt. . . . Und so,' he say, 'Fritz, olt friendt, God bless you und keep you verefer you are . . . in eferyting you do. . . . Our hearts go mit you und you leaf a blace dat no vun else can efer fill.'"

Mr. Helm paused a moment, checked by the powerful swelling flood of his own feeling, and in the silence my father cleared his throat a little huskily, straightened gauntly in his chair, wet his great thumb briefly, and muttered: "Ah, Lord!"

"Den he gif to me," the old man went on quietly in a moment, "a check for five hundert dollars . . . ja!" – his voice rose strongly with an emphasis of passion – "*five hundert dollars!* . . . A bresent dat dey make to me dis time because dey know I go for good! . . . Und de odders gif to me a luffing-cup . . . und efery month of my life now, as lonk as I lif, – it comes to me a pension of two hundert dollars – and if I die – if I should be de first to go," he went on in a shaking voice, "den de pension comes to Else just de same."

He stopped, and in the darkness I could hear the hungry feeding silence of the boarders, and in a moment heard my father come back sharply in his chair, spit hard and wide, clear his throat and say:

"Ah, Lord! That was a noble act! It does you good to hear it! It goes to show that all mercy, justice, truth, and honor is not dead on earth. It was 'Well done, thou good and faithful servant!' with a vengeance! That's what it was, all right!" And savagely he cleared his throat again, lunged forward in his chair and spat across the rail, lunged back, and in the darkness I could feel the boarders waiting.

"Ja," said Mr. Helm, quietly, with a tranquil certitude, "dat vas it. All my life I haf been faithful to dem – und dey vere fine to me! If you are faithful all goes vell," he said, and silent for a moment, he lifted his cigar to tranquil lips and smoked.

"I vork for dem for ofer forty years," he said. "Ven I go dere first it vas de time ven Hayes vas Bresident. . . . Dot vas a lonk lonk time ago," said old man Helm, and smoked.

"Ah, Lord!" my father answered gravely. "That it was! A long, long time! And well do I remember!"

He lunged forward in his chair again and spat strongly, cleanly out across the rail into the dark geranium bed, and the boarders waited. Then, for a moment, there was nothing but the brooding silence of cool, lilac and deep-breasted night, a woman's laughter welling soft and low and sensual from the darkness of a summer porch, and somewhere far away a motor starting, racing and receding into night's dark and secret heart, then silence, mystery, and the earth again.

That was the year the war came.

* * * * * * *

Then, as the boarders waited, my father spoke again of the old times, the vanished faces, the lost men. He spoke of all the wars and troubles he had known, told how he had stood, "a barefoot country boy," beside a dusty road twelve miles from Gettysburg, and had watched the dusty ragged rebels march past upon the road that led to death and battle and the shipwreck of their hopes.

He spoke of the faint and ominous trembling of the guns across the hot and brooding silence of the countryside, and how silence, wonder, and unspoken questions filled the hearts of all the people, and how they had gone about their work upon the farm as usual. He spoke of the years that followed on the war when he was a stonecutter's apprentice in Baltimore, and he spoke of ancient joys and labors, forgotten acts and histories, and he spoke then with familiar memory of the lost Americans— —

My father spoke then of the strange, lost, time-far, dead Americans, the remote, voiceless, and bewhiskered faces of the great Americans, who were more lost to me than Egypt, more far from me than the Tartarian coasts, more haunting strange than Cipango or the lost faces of the first dynastic kings that built the Pyramids – whom he had seen, heard, known, found familiar in the full pulse and passion and proud glory of his terrific youth. My father spoke of the lost, time-far, voiceless faces of Buchanan, Johnson, Douglas, Tilden, Blaine – the proud, vacant, time-strange, and bewhiskered visages of Garfield, Arthur, Harrison and Hayes.

"Ah, Lord!" he said – his voice went out in darkness like a gong. "Ah, Lord! – I've known all of 'em since James Buchanan's time – for I was a boy of six when he took office!"

Here he paused a moment, lunged forward violently in his rocking chair, and spat cleanly out a spurt of strong tobacco juice across the porch-rail into the loamy earth, the night-sweet fragrance of the geranium beds.

"Yes, sir," he said gravely, lunging back again, while the attentive, hungry boarders waited in the living darkness and were still – "I remember all of them since James Buchanan's time, and I've seen most of them that came since Lincoln's day! Ah, Lord!" – he paused briefly for another waiting moment, shaking his grave head sadly in the dark – "Well do I remember the day when I stood on a street in Baltimore – poor friendless orphan that I was!" my father went on sorrowfully, but somewhat imprecisely since, at the time he mentioned, his mother was alive and in good health, upon her little farm in Pennsylvania, and would continue so for almost fifty years – "a poor friendless country boy of sixteen years, alone in the great city where I had come to learn my trade as an apprentice – and heard Andrew Johnson, then the president of this *great* nation," said my father, "speak from the platform of a horse-car – and he was so drunk – so *drunk!*" – he howled – "the president of this country was so *drunk* that they had to stand on both sides of him and prop him up – or he'd a-gone head over heels into the gutter!"

Here he paused, wet his great thumb briefly, cleared his throat with considerable satisfaction, lunged forward violently again in his rocking chair and spat cleanly, strongly forth a wad of bright tobacco juice into the loamy fragrance of the dark geranium bed.

"The first vote I ever cast for president," my father continued presently, as he lunged back again, "I cast in eighteen hundred and seventy-two, in Baltimore, for that g r e a t man – that brave and noble soldier – U. S. Grant!"

"Ja!" said Mr. Helm, nodding vigorously. "I vote for him dat time! Dot vas de first time dot I vote! Ven I come from Chermany dere vas de var, und den I could not vote."

"And I have voted for every Republican nominee for president ever since," my father said. "I voted for Rutherford B. Hayes of Ohio in 1876 – that was the year, as you well know, of the great Hayes-Tilden controversy."

"Controversy, was it?" said McKeithan, the jeweller's assistant, good-naturedly enough, but with an evident undertone of cynical disparagement. "You can call it controversy if you like, but some people call it highway robbery."

My father, impatient with the interruption, cleared his throat loudly and rapidly, rocked violently back and forth in his chair, breathing heavily, made no answer.

"Now I don't care what you say – *that* man got elected," said McKeithan stubbornly, but with an appearance of good nature through which,
however, the ugly truculence of his distempered spirit showed furious,
bare, and ugly. "Yes, sir!" he declared with an obstinate finality, bringing
his feet down from the porch rail to the porch in a sudden, nervous,
almost furious movement of distemper, although he still maintained his
strained pretense of hearty amiability. "By rights, he should have been the
president of this country, but the Republicans cheated him out of it!"

My father cleared his throat, hitched impatiently in his chair, wet his
thumb, and said shortly: "He was defeated by Hayes, who was given a
majority of one vote by the electoral commission – all of which is provided
for under the terms of the Federal Constitution."

Mr. Helm nodded his head slowly with the devoted affirmation he gave
to all of my father's opinions. "Ja," he said. "Dot iss righd! I gan remember."

"I don't care what you can remember," said McKeithan, laughing and
shaking his head rapidly as he stared downward at the floor with the ugly
brainless obstinacy of the provincial Southerner. The note of fury and distemper in his voice was more naked, plain and ugly now than it had been
before. "All I say is that they cheated that man out of his election after he'd
won it fair and square."

Then he laughed again, his sudden full agreeable laugh of South Carolina good nature that had in it something ugly, false, and shameful because it came so quick and palpably to cover up the image of the naked
and malevolent hatred that sweltered in him and that blazed furiously out
of his watery red eyes even as he laughed.

He was a man in his late thirties, but his black abundant hair, which
he parted in the middle, was already coarsely and heavily streaked with
grey. He had sharply defined, but rather generous and pleasant-looking
features. It was a thin, seamed, nervous-looking face, marked strongly with
the quick, thin, febrile, hotly sensitive alertness of the Southerner, and yet
rather agreeable and engaging, save for the over-developed rocky muscu-
larity of the jaw muscles, which writhed and twisted almost constantly, sug-
gesting unpleasantly the desperate and tenuous effort at control of a man
who is suffering from a whole hell of jangled, gnarled and abscessed nerves
which may twist out of his grasp at any moment.

His figure was tall, thin, almost fragile, and the nervous, almost con-
vulsive, quickness of his movements also suggested the enforced and tortured control of the habitual alcoholic. He was always neatly and carefully

dressed in garments which were not gaudy but which showed a rather provincial and local taste in favor of colored sox, tan shoes, shirts and neckties moderately striped, tie-clasps, engraved belt buckles, and elegant-looking watch fobs.

He smoked cigarettes constantly, but with a kind of deep-drawn languorous inhalation that I had noticed a thousand times in the small-town South Carolinian, and which was one of the most agreeable things on earth to watch, and which gave a kind of rare sensual quality even to the most common men of that region, beside which the middle-westerner, for instance, would seem flat, colorless and rather dreary. It evoked a powerful sensuous image of an easy-going pleasure-loving race who were able to draw ease, luxury, and delight from the most common and uncostly pleasures of the earth, and to touch every familiar act and experience of life, food, tobacco, drinking, going on a journey or to a baseball game, or sitting on a porch step talking to one of their slow-tongued sweet-voiced women with a brooding, sultry, entrail-stirring prophecy of exultant joy.

In addition to this, McKeithan had the infinitely engaging and agreeable tone and manner of these people: the soft, low-toned friendly voice, the natural grace and easiness of manner, the instinctive desire for warm, friendly and happy relations with people, the native, almost excusable, hypocrisy of agreeableness which marks the Southerner, and the sudden, genial, deep-toned laugh of good-natured friendliness.

It was an image of the natural sensuous man as warm, engaging and attractive as anything on earth could be, if one could have found the same complement of warmth, freedom, friendliness and natural vigor in the soul. But one rarely found that dual triumph in these people: behind its warmly colored and attractive tenement of flesh, the soul looked out warped, mutilated, full of fear, ignorance, cruelty, superstition and mistrust.

And so it was with McKeithan. Even as he laughed his sudden, warm, deep-noted laugh, and spoke in his agreeable low voice to you, his inflamed and reddened eyes were looking at you all the time with an ugly, sullen, furious and distempered look, in which all the blind distempered hatred of his mutilated soul was packed. Yet no one could pluck out the heart of this mystery. We did not know the reason for this poisonous hatred of the soul in which his life was drowning, and though he saw it, felt it, lived it hideously with every anguished breath he drew, it is certain he did not know the cause or remedy himself.

Now I could hear his right foot doing it's devil's jig upon the porch, and I knew that he was crossing and uncrossing his thin legs rapidly and convulsively in an effort to check the dissonant almost epileptic jerking of his limbs, and that his head was craning, jerking, and grimacing over the edges of his collar like a man suffering from some uncontrollable disease of the facial nerves, and that there was nothing constant but the blind, sweltering, and implacable hatred in his inflamed red eyes.

What was it? What was the reason for that terrible distemper of the spirit, that maddened fury and unrest of soul that was so different from my father's since it seemed to work like poison in the blood, to have no name or aim or reason in its blind unarguable insanity of hate? What had caused the horrible dissonance of nerves, brain, heart, mind, spirit in this man which had already wrecked his life and within another year would utterly destroy him. For, one morning eight months later while lying in the lower berth of a Pullman coming south from Washington – whither he had gone and been rejected in a final fruitless effort to enlist for active service in the army – he shot himself through the brain, dying as he had lived, a ruined, lost, and desperate man, with the reason for his life's grief and error unknown.

Later, I could not forget the man. The memory of his life and death, and the fury of blind brainless hatred that could blaze so suddenly from his reddened eyes would return to haunt my spirit with a wordless pity and regret. The man's life must have been one agony of living hell – a hell from which no one on earth could save him, and from which he had no power to save himself. And curiously, although I never knew the reason for the cancerous poison of the soul that was destroying him, I seemed to understand its nature thoroughly. For I had felt its sweltering corrosions in myself, and seen it in a thousand other men.

And for this reason I could not forget him. For, although part of the distempered weather of his life, the moroseness, mistrust, and sudden taking of offense when no offense had been intended, was traceable to his constant saturation in the fatal anodyne of alcohol – a saturation so complete that it never rose to open drunkenness and never knew a cleansing interval of sobriety – that enslavement was itself not the cause of the destroying malady, but one of the results.

Moreover, I had seen all the elements of that disease – the lacerated, swiftly-wounded pride, the sudden blind hostility, the stubborn, ugly and dogmatic prejudice, the truculent flaring-up in face of an imagined injury, the wild, blind, maddened hatreds of the soul – in a thousand other South-ern men, and particularly in those who came, as did McKeithan, from a region where cruelty, fear and ignorance were rooted in the structure of man's life, where the free play and exploration of man's spirit was warped and mutilated from his birth, and where the only alternative to the un-questioning and utter conformity that was demanded to the dogmas of that life, no matter how cruel, superstitious and degrading they might be, was exile, bitter and dishonored loneliness, or death.

Thus, in the eyes of a thousand other men from those same regions, of whom McKeithan might have been the brother, so much was he their true type in look, in soft-toned and agreeable speech, in natural kindliness, friendliness, warmth and grace of manner, I had seen that same look of blind, ugly, reasonless and distempered hate. It seemed to come from something fierce and lonely in their lives, from something so foully poi-soned and grievously lacerated that their lives had become one incurable running wound of passionate bitterness and disgust, one maddened griev-ance of complaint against an insult, injury and injustice for which they had no words.

Thus, I knew that McKeithan was now sitting in the darkness on the porch, choking with feelings of hatred, revenge, and insulted pride, all because my father had made a simple reference to the old Hayes-Tilden controversy. And by this time, also, although in what way he could him-self not have determined, that simple reference to Hayes and Tilden had become so poisonously enlarged and translated in McKeithan's maddened brain that he had now read into it an insult implied or intended for him-self, so that he now found some sneer at his judgment, some intolerable insult to his dignity and pride, in any word of simple disagreement.

And now the madness of blind hate had so possessed him that he sat there in the darkness drowning in his venom, doing his devil's jig upon the floor with one frantic foot, jerking and twitching like the victim of an epileptic fit, smiling convulsively, and bursting from time to time into an ugly jeering laugh from which every vestige of good nature had vanished, as he read into every word my father, Mr. Helm or anyone else now said, a sneer or insult intended for himself.

In the same way, the man had suddenly begun to hate me one night in winter two years before, although I was only a boy of fourteen years at that time, and had never done or intended to do him any injury. We had been sitting round the table in the dining room one Sunday night in

February, and my father, who had been talking about Gladstone, now quoted one of his favorite sayings: that Gladstone, on being asked by a foreigner the population of England, had answered: "About fifteen million, mostly fools."

For some reason, probably because I had for the first time that winter read *A Midsummer Night's Dream*, this suggested to me the famous utterance of Puck – "Lord! What fools these mortals be!"

When this happened, Mr. McKeithan, who had been eating in silence, smiling bitterly and morosely to himself while he ate, now broke into an ugly jeering laugh, and said:

"Yes, and some of the fools are sitting not very far away from me right now!"

Then, even as we stared at the man in gape-mouthed stupefaction, he suddenly hurled his knife and fork down on the table, pushed back his chair violently, leaped to his feet, and glaring across the table at me, he cried in a shaking voice: –

"You – you – you – damned fellow, you! – I'm not going to stand for your insults any longer!"

And suddenly he rushed around the table towards me, his face livid and convulsed, his eyes blood-shot and blind with hate. I jumped to my feet, badly shocked and frightened by his unprovoked and reasonless assault. As I did so, the man rushed on me and struck out at me with his opened hands, a clumsy and feeble blow that did me no harm but that sent me back a foot or two. I hit back at him from a kind of instinct and my blow was harder and more solid – it caught him on the breast and sent him staggering back.

A wretched and degraded scene had then occurred which even at that time, with all the excitement and anger that I felt, had seemed shameful to me, and which later I could not forget. For, although even at that time I had been bigger and stronger than the man, and better able to defend myself, I had felt so powerfully the contaminating shame of his act, the naked ruin in his life that had made him so forget his manhood as to come to blows with a boy of fourteen years, who had never done him any injury, that I could hardly bear to look at him.

And at the same time I felt a horrible and nauseous sickness as if that poisonous and morbid disease of his own nerves, the huge infection of his own life, had somehow tainted all the wholesome tissues of my life and spirit, so that suddenly the lights turned dull and wretched like a smear of blood, and for a moment I seemed to have the thick brown taste of blood and shame and loathing in my mouth.

The man had stood there, mad with fear and rage and shame, knowing that he had now irrevocably stripped bare to our gaze of horror the festering sore of his life. Stripped of the last rag of concealment, he now railed wildly, miserably, at all of us, trembling in every limb as if he had the palsy, and shouting at us accusations of insults and injuries we had never done to him in a voice that shook, faltered, gasped and choked and was finally almost incoherent:

"This – this – this – fellow!" he panted, pointing a shaking finger at me. "Ever since I came here – it's been one thing after another – I've taken as much as I can stand from this – this – this – damned boy –"

And finally, we had said nothing to him, but had just stood looking at him, silent and full of a horrible anguish of regret and shame until he had gasped himself to silence. During all the time the man had railed at us, my mother had stood solidly, quietly, her strong worn hands clasped at her waist in their powerful loose gesture, her powerful and delicate mouth puckered in an expression of strong revulsion and concern.

When he had finished, she said nothing, but just looked at him quietly for a moment, shaking her head silently and slightly from side to side in a movement of powerful and spontaneous regret. That natural, simple, and wordless gesture had suddenly overwhelmed the man with the shame and despair as no words of anger or reproach could do. He had stared at my mother for a moment with his inflamed eyes and trembling speechless lips, and suddenly had turned with a scream of pain like the cry of a tortured animal, and had rushed out of the room and up the stairs, shouting:

"I'll not put up with any more of it. . . . I'm going to leave – do you hear?"

Within fifteen minutes he had come down again carrying a valise packed with his few belongings, had spoken quietly to her and paid his bill, and then had gone. Three months later he came back to us again. He never spoke to any of us about the quarrel, and none of us spoke to him about it. The elements of shame and pity made us silent. After that, his manner towards me was as kind, friendly, and good-natured as anyone's could be. But when he looked at me his reddened eyes were full of the blind unreasoning hatred. It was the hatred of a man who knows the hatred that exposed him had no reason, and who hates more bitterly on that account.

Now, I knew, he was sitting there in the darkness, completely out of reason, choked with hate, sweltering in corroding meditation of his imagined wrongs. It is doubtful if he was any longer able to pay attention to what was being said by the other people. Rather, he sat there brewing in his own poison, with twitching limbs and a convulsed and livid face, hearing from time to time a random word or phrase, muttering "Yeah" from time to time and laughing to himself an ugly jeering laugh.

Now I could hear my father's voice again. Less annoyed by argument, to which he paid no attention anyway, than by the interruption, he now cleared his throat and said in a tone of almost comic patience and long-suffering resignation:

"Well – am I to be allowed to speak, or not – or must I always be interrupted when I start?"

Several of the boarders could now be heard hitching their chairs around eagerly, and murmuring hastily, as if there was an enormous passive vacancy in their own lives, forever famished and unfed, and waiting to be filled: "No, go on, go on. We want to hear about it." Then I could hear old Mr. Helm's guttural voice speaking in tones of chiding reproof, as he ponderously defended the inviolable right to speech of his hero:

"Den you should all keep k'viet und not interrupt," he said severely. "Dere are t'ings de rest of you don't know aboud."

"All right! All right!" said Mr. McKeithan, laughing his full sudden hearty laugh of false good-nature. "No one's stopping you! Go on!"

"Well, as I say," my father said then, clearing his throat and wetting his great thumb briefly on his mouth, "the first vote that I cast was for U. S. Grant in 1872, I voted for Hayes in 1876, in 1880 I cast my vote for James Abram Garfield – that *great* good man," he passionately declared, "that martyred hero who was so foully and brutally done to death by the cowardly assault of a murderous assasin!"

"You're sure it wasn't a Democrat who murdered him?" said McKeithan with his full, false, ugly laugh.

"He did not say it vas a Democrat," said Mr. Helm heavily.

"No, but I thought it was only the Democrats who committed crimes," McKeithan answered. "When anything good gets done it's always done by the Republicans. Isn't that right?" He laughed jeeringly again and relapsed bitterly and sullenly into the huge self-poison that was drowning him.

My father breathed heavily and impatiently, like a locomotive checked in its full course until some obstacle that lay across the rails had been removed. Then he cleared his throat, wet his thumb, lunged forward in his rocking chair and spat, and went on without paying any further attention to his heckler.

"In 1884," he said, "I cast my vote for James G. Blaine in the year that Grover Cleveland defeated him – "

"Something must have been wrong that time," McKeithan said now with an ugly laugh. "That was the time the Democrats got in. That time doesn't count."

"They got in," my father answered shortly, "because Blaine let Burchard's 'Rum Romanism and Rebellion' speech go unchallenged. It was a fatal error, if ever there was one! It turned the Roman Catholic vote against him like a flash. And that was the thing that defeated him. But he'd have been elected by a big majority had it not been for that speech! You can rest assured of that!" my father said, and spat.

"I voted for Benjamin Harrison in 1888, and for Harrison again in 1892 – the time that Cleveland got in for his second term – "

"Ah – hah," said McKeithan ironically and then laughed his false and ugly laugh again. "What went wrong that time?"

"Everything," my father answered curtly, "as anyone who was alive then and remembers it could tell you. That was a time we will remember to our dying days," he went on grimly. "Business went to smash, the banks were going to the wall – "

"Ja," said Mr. Helm, "I gan remember dat: de banks are glosing all around us – de people are all frightened und dey make a run on us – dey come pooshing in like dey vas crazy – 'Vere iss my money?' – ve gif it to dem – ve are vaiting in de cage mit shtacks of it dat high," he added, indicating its height with a comical gesture of his pudgy hands. "It last for t'ree days und den dey go avay. Ve vere too shtrong for dem," he concluded proudly. "But dat vas a bad time!"

"A fearful time!" my father said. "There was no work, no business, no money, and no nothing, for the Democrats were in and we had soup-kitchens. . . . And you can mark my words," he howled suddenly, "you'll have them again, before these next four years are over – your guts will grease your back-bone as sure as there's a God in heaven before that fearful, that awful, that cruel, inhuman and blood-thirsty monster – who kept us out of war" – he snarled bitterly – "is done with you! For hell, ruin, misery, and damnation commences every time the Democrats get in. You can rest assured of that!" he said, and breathing heavily with excitement he lunged forward in his chair and spat and then rocked violently for a moment, his great hands gripped hard on the arms of the rocking chair.

"Oh, here, here, here! Papa, for heaven's sake!" – for the first time now I could hear my sister's voice, speaking to him quietly, wearily humorous, with patient and tolerant reproof. She had been married just the year before, and that summer, after a year's absence, she and her husband had returned home to live, to keep life in my father while she could.

"You mustn't talk that way!" she said quietly, laughing. "He's just the same as everybody else, and trying to do the best he can – even if he is a Democrat. Besides," she now said warningly, almost angrily, "you can't afford to talk that way! You're going to get yourself in trouble if you don't look out! That talk was all right a year ago, but, good heavens, Papa!" – she now cried with a furious impatience – "this country's at war now! Can't you realize that? We're not a neutral nation any longer. You've already got one son in the navy and before it's over the rest of them may have to join up, too. If people hear you say these things they'll think you're pro-German!"

No one spoke for a moment and then old Mr. Helm said doggedly:

"Dere iss vorse t'ings in de vorld dan being Cherman! Dere iss as goot Cherman people as any vun!"

"Why, of course there are, Mr. Helm," my sister now said kindly. "I know there are! I wasn't casting any reflections on you, at all. Besides I never thought of you as being German – I always thought of you as an American."

"Ja," said Mr. Helm slowly and heavily, "I am an American – as goot an American as anyvun. But I vas also born in Chermany und all my beeple come from dere. De Kaiser iss a bat man – I do not say dat he iss not. All de time he vants to fight und he make all dis trouble! But de Cherman people iss all righd – as goot people as you vill find anyvere."

"They have been," my father said, clearing his throat, "among the finest citizens we have – and now it is a fearful, cruel, damnable and hellish thing that we should be called upon by that inhuman monster to go out and shoot down our own flesh and blood – for that's what it amounts to in the end."

"Ja," said Mr. Helm emphatically. "Dot iss righd!"

"Well, I know," my sister said with weary patience. "That may be true enough. There may be lots of us who feel that way, but we're at war with them now and they're our enemies. So you mustn't talk like that. People don't understand that kind of talk! You'll get yourself in trouble!" she said sternly.

My father said nothing, but for a moment he rocked back and forth furiously, muttered under his breath, cleared his throat savagely once or twice as if about to speak, and then spat vigorously out across the rail. He had, as a matter of fact, until the outbreak of the war, been one of the most violent critics of President Wilson's peace-time policies, had howled bitterly at the sinking of the ships and all the other insults to the nation's outraged honor. Yes, in his recent patriotic frenzy he had fairly panted for satisfaction, painting a thrilling picture of what "Teddy would have done" had he been in office.

Under the formidable threats of twenty-four-hour ultimatums instantly dispatched, of armies, fleets and expeditions ready to set sail "at an instant's notice," my father saw the insolent enemy cringing into immediate submission and retreat – "as he made them do in the Venezuela dispute in 1904," he howled, "when he told them he would order the fleet to set sail instantly if they did not withdraw their forces!" It was a splendid image of that proud lost world of San Juan Hill and cock-crow patriotism which would, my father thought, be magically brought to life again if only Teddy could be there to tell them how.

But suddenly, as instantly as it had flared, the fire was gone, and my father was an old man again. Even in the howling anathema of his attack on Wilson, there had been something different from the savage partisanship of other days – the days of Cleveland, Blaine, and Roosevelt – the strange lost days of Garfield, Arthur, Harrison and Hayes. There had been, in this new feeling of my father's, something more personal and bitter, the hatred of an old man who is dying in a new world he no longer knows and understands and for whom, somehow, the unfamiliar forms of that new world are allied in his frenzy to the hated form of death.

Therefore he curses and reviles them in his sorrow and despair as if somehow "they" – unknown, cruel, and phantasmal "they" that will not let us live or give us rest – have done his life to death. My father had lived life with so fierce a love, and now he died so bitterly with such wild regret that it was a rending anguish of the soul to see him die, a horror that we could not forget.

But now, as if he too had suddenly felt the huge indifference of despair, and knew that the world he had so passionately evoked was lost to him forever, all of the fire had gone out of him and he was an old man again, sick

James A. Garfield,
twentieth president of
the United States.
*Courtesy of the
Library of Congress*

and dying, the enfeebled ghost of his past strength sunken in a phantasmal memory – lost in the sorrowful shades of a world that I could never
know, and that had gone from him forever.

"Ah, Lord!" my father said at length sadly, gravely, in a low almost
inaudible tone. All the old life and howling fury of his rhetoric had gone
from him: he was an old man again, sick, indifferent, dying, and his voice
had grown worn, weary, old, and sad.

"Ah, Lord!" he muttered again, shaking his head sadly, thinly, wearily
in the dark, "I've seen them come and go: Buchanan, Lincoln, Johnson,
Tilden, Blaine . . . Garfield, Arthur, Harrison and Hayes . . . and all . . .
all . . . all of them are dead. . . . All, all are gone – the old familiar faces –
I'm the only one that's left," he said illogically, "and soon I'll be gone, too."

Then for a moment he was silent as the tidal flood of time, dark time,
strange time that haunts us with the briefness of our days, swept over him.
"It's been a long time – a long, long time," he muttered. "It's pretty strange
when you come to think of it. By God it is!" And he was silent, and darkness, the huge enfolding mystery of great-starred night was all about us.

Garfield, Arthur, Harrison and Hayes – time of my father's time, earth
of his earth, blood of his blood, life of his life – living, real, and actual

people in all the passion, power, and feeling of my father's youth. And for me, the lost Americans: their gravely vacant and bewhiskered faces mixed, melted, swam together in the sea-depths of a past intangible, immeasurable, and unknowable as the buried city of Persepolis.

And they were lost.

* * * * * * *

For who was Garfield, martyred man, and who had seen him in the streets of life? Who could believe his footfalls ever sounded on a lonely pavement? Who had heard the casual and familiar tones of Chester Arthur? And where was Harrison? Where was Hayes? Which had the whiskers, which the burnsides: which was which?

Were they not lost?

Into their ears, as ours, the tumults of forgotten crowds, upon their brains the million printings of lost time, and suddenly upon their dying sight the brief bitter pain and joy of a few death-bright, fixed and fading memories: – the twisting of a leaf upon a bough, the grinding felloe-rim against the curb, the long distant and retreating thunder of a train upon the rails.

Garfield, Hayes, and Harrison were Ohio men; but only the name of Garfield had been brightened by his blood. But at night had they not heard the howlings of demented wind, the sharp, clean, windy rain of the acorns? Had all of them not walked down lonely roads at night in winter and seen a light and known it was theirs? Had all of them not known the wilderness?

Had they not known the smell of old bound calf and well-worn leathers, the Yankee lawyer's smell of strong tobacco spit and court-house urinals, the smell of horses, harness, men and sweating country men, of jury rooms and court rooms – the strong male smell of Justice at the county seat, and heard a tap along dark corridors where fell a drop in darkness with a punctual crescent monotone of time, dark time.

Had not Garfield, Hayes, and Harrison studied law in offices with a dark brown smell? Had not the horses trotted past below their windows in wreaths of dust along a straggling street of shacks and buildings with false fronts? Had they not heard below them the voices of men talking, loitering up in drawling heat? Had they not heard the casual, rich-fibred, faintly howling country voices, and heard the rustling of a woman's skirt, and waiting silence, slily lowered tones of bawdry and then huge guffaws, slapped meaty thighs, and high fat choking laughter? And in the dusty dozing heat, while time buzzed slowly, like a fly, had not Garfield, Arthur, Harrison and Hayes then smelled the river, the humid, subtly fresh, half-rotten river, and thought of the white flesh of the women then beside the river, and felt a slow impending passion in their entrails, a heavy rending power in their hands?

Then Garfield, Arthur, Harrison and Hayes had gone to war, and each became a brigadier or major-general. All were bearded men: they saw a spattering of bright blood upon the leaves, and they heard the soldiers talking in the dark of food and women. They held the bridge-head in bright dust at places with such names as Wilson's Creek and Spangler's Spring, and their men smashed cautiously through dense undergrowth. And they had heard the surgeons cursing after battles and the little rasp of saws. They had seen boys standing awkwardly holding their entrails in their hands, and pleading pitifully with fear-bright eyes: "Is it bad, General? Do you think it's bad?"

When the canister came through it made a ragged hole. It smashed through tangled leaves and boughs, sometimes it plunked solidly into the fibre of a tree. Sometimes when it struck a man it tore away the roof of his brain, the wall of his skull, raggedly, so that his brains seethed out upon a foot of wilderness, and the blood blackened and congealed, and he lay there in his thick clumsy uniform, with a smell of urine in the wool, in the casual awkward and incompleted attitude of sudden death. And when Garfield, Arthur, Harrison and Hayes saw these things they saw that it was not like the picture they had had, as children, it was not like the works of Walter Scott and William Gilmore Simms. They saw that the hole was not clean and small and in the central front, and the field was not green nor fenced, nor mown. Over the vast and immemorable earth the quivering heated light of afternoon was shining, a field swept rudely upward to a lift of rugged wood, and field by field, gulley by gulch by fold, the earth advanced in rude, sweet, limitless convolutions.

Then Garfield, Arthur, Harrison and Hayes had paused by the bridge-head for a moment and were still, seeing the bright blood at noon upon the trampled wheat, feeling the brooding hush of three o'clock across the fields where all the storming feet had passed at dawn, seeing the way the rough field hedge leaned out across the dusty road, the casual intrusions of the coarse field grasses and the hot dry daisies to the edges of the road, seeing the rock-bright sallows of the creek, the sweet cool shade and lean of river trees across the water.

Chester A. Arthur,
twenty-first president
of the United States.
*Courtesy of the
Library of Congress*

They paused then by the bridge-head looking at the water. They saw the stark blank flatness of the old red mill, that somehow was like sunset, coolness, sorrow and delight, and looked at the faces of dead boys among the wheat – the most-oh-most familiar, plain, the death-strange faces of the dead Americans – they stood there for a moment, thinking, feeling, thinking, with strong, wordless wonder in their hearts:

"There is the bridge we crossed, the mill we slept in, and the creek. There is a field of wheat, a hedge, a dusty road, an apple orchard and the sweet wild tangle of a wood upon that hill. And there is six o'clock across the fields, again now and always as it was and will be to world's end forever. And some of us have died this morning coming through the field – and that was time – time – time. We shall not come again, we never shall come back again, we never shall come back along this road again as we did once at morning – so, brothers, let us look again before we go. . . . There is the mill, and there the hedge, and there the sallows of the rock-bright waters of the creek, and there the sweet and most familiar coolness of the trees – and surely we have been this way before!" they cried.

"Oh, surely, brothers, we have sat upon the bridge, before the mill, and sung together by the rock-bright waters of the creek at evening, and came across the wheat field in the morning and heard the dew-sweet bird-song rising from the hedge before! O plain, O most-familiar and most homely earth, proud earth of this huge land unutterable, proud nobly swelling earth, in all your delicacy, wildness, savagery, and terror – grand earth in all your loveliness, beauty and exultant joy, terrific earth in all your limit-less fecundities, swelling with infinite fold and convolution into the reaches of the west forever – American earth! – bridge, hedge and creek and dusty road – you plain tremendous poetry of Wilson's Creek where boys died in the wheat this morning – O you unutterable far-near, strange-familiar, homely earth of magic, for which a word would do if we could find it, for which a word would do if we could call it by its name, for which a word would do that never can be spoken, that can never be forgotten, and that will never be revealed – O proud, familiar, nobly swelling earth, it seems we must have known you before! It seems we must have known you forever, but all we know for certain is that we came along this road one time at morning, and now our blood is painted on the wheat, and you are ours now, we are yours forever – and there is something here we never shall remember – oh, there is something here we never shall forget!"

* * * * * * * *

[Hearing my father's voice then on the porch, I thought:] had Garfield, Arthur, Harrison and Hayes been young? Or had they all been born with flowing whiskers, sideburns, and wing collars, speaking gravely from the cradle of their mothers' arms the noble vacant sonorities of far-seeing states-manship? It could not be. Had they not all been young men in the Thir-ties, the Forties, and the Fifties? Did they not, as we, cry out at night along deserted roads into demented winds? Did they not, as we, cry out the fierce goat-cry of ecstasy and exultancy, as the full measure of their hunger, their potent and inchoate hope, went out into that single wordless cry?

Did they not, as we, when young, prowl softly up and down the door-less avenues of night, seeing the gas lamps flare and flutter on the corner, falling with livid light upon the corners of old cobbled streets of brown-stone houses? Had they not heard the lonely rhythmic clopping of a horse, the jounting wheels of a hansom cab, upon those barren cobbles? And had they not waited, waited, trembling in the darkness till the horse and cab had passed, had vanished with the lonely recession of shod hooves, and then were heard no more?

And then had Garfield, Arthur, Harrison and Hayes not waited, waited in the silence of the night, prowling up and down the lonely cobbled street, with trembling lips, numb entrails, pounding hearts? Had they not set their jaws, made sudden indecisive movements, felt terror, joy, a numb impending ecstasy, and had waited, waited then – for what? Had they not waited, hearing sounds of shifting engines in the yards at night, hearing the hoarse, gaseous breaths of little engines through the grimy fan-flare of their funnels, the racketing clack of wheels upon the light, ill-laid, ill-joined rails? Had they not waited there in that dark street with the fierce lone hunger of a boy, feeling around them the immense and moving quietness of sleep, the heart beats of ten thousand sleeping men, as they waited, waited, waited in the night?

Had they not, as we, then turned their eyes up and seen the huge starred vision of the night, the immense and lilac darkness of America and April? Had they not heard the sudden, shrill, and piping whistle of a departing engine? Had they not waited, thinking, feeling, seeing then the immense mysterious continent of night, the wild and lyric earth, so casual, sweet, and strange-familiar, in all its space and savagery and terror, its mystery and joy, its limitless sweep and rudeness, its delicate and savage fecundity? Had they not had a vision of the plains, the mountains, and the rivers flowing in the darkness, the huge pattern of the everlasting earth and the all-engulfing wilderness of America?

Had they not felt, as we have felt, as they waited in the night, the huge lonely earth of night time and America, on which ten thousand lonely sleeping little towns were strewn? Had they not seen the fragile network of the light, racketing, ill-joined little rails across the land, over which the lonely little trains rushed on in darkness, flinging a handful of lost echoes at the river's edge, leaving an echo in the cut's resounding cliff, and being engulfed then in huge lonely night, in all-brooding, all-engulfing night? Had they not known, as we have known, the wild secret joy and mystery of the everlasting earth, the lilac dark, the savage, silent, all-possessing wilderness that gathered in around ten thousand lonely little towns, ten million lost and lonely sleepers, and waited, and abode forever, and was still?

Had not Garfield, Arthur, Harrison and Hayes then waited, feeling the goat-cry swelling in their throats, feeling wild joy and sorrow in their hearts, and a savage hunger and desire – a flame, a fire, a fury – burning fierce and lean and lonely in the night, burning forever while the sleepers slept? Were they not burning, burning, burning, even as the rest of us have burned? Were Garfield, Arthur, Harrison and Hayes not burning in the night? Were they not burning forever in the silence of the little towns with

Benjamin Harrison,
twenty-third president of
the United States.
Courtesy of the Library of Congress

all the fierce hunger, savage passion, limitless desire that young men in this land have known in the darkness?

Were they not burning with the wild and wordless hope, the incredible belief that all young men have known before the wild promise of that huge mirage, the deathless dupe and invincible illusion of this savage all-exultant land where all things are impending and where young men starve? Were they not burning in the enfabled magic, mystery, and exultant joy of lilac dark, the lonely, savage, secret, everlasting earth on which we lived, and wrought, and perished, mad with hunger, unfed, famished, furious, unassuaged? Were they not burning, burning where a million doors of glory, love, unutterable fulfilment, impended, waited in the dark for us, were here, were here around us in the dark forever, were here beside us in the dark forever, were ready to our touch forever, and that duped us, mocked forever at our hunger, maddened our hearts and brains with searching, took our youth, our strength, our love, our life, and killed us, and were never found?

Had Garfield, Arthur, Harrison and Hayes not waited then, as we have waited, with numb lips and pounding hearts and fear, delight, exultancy and terror stirring in their entrails as they waited in the silent street before the shuttered windows of a house, proud, evil, lavish, lighted, certain, secret, and alone? And as they heard the hoof, the wheel, the sudden whistle and the immense and sleeping silence of the town, the lonely, wild exultant earth, the lilac dark, the huge starred visage of the night – did they not wait there in the darkness thinking:

"Oh, there are new lands, morning, and a shining city. Soon, soon, soon!"

And thinking, feeling, thinking, with wild secret joy, intolerable desire, as they heard the sudden shrill departure of the whistle: "There are women in the West and we shall find them. [Coming at evening to their door, a wanderer, we shall find them standing there with quiet eyes.] They will be waiting for us, calm, tranquil, corn-haired, lavish, unsurprised, looking across the wall of level grain with level eyes, looking into the flaming domains of the red, the setting sun, at the great wall, and the soaring vistas of the western ranges. "Oh, there are lavish, corn-haired women in the West with tranquil eyes!" cried Garfield, Arthur, Harrison and Hayes, "and we shall find them waiting in their doors for us at evening! [Then we shall base our heads upon the limitless depth, the snowy purity and the proud sustentions of their Atlantean breasts, lie cradled in the fragrant whiteness of their swelling and columnar thighs, possess the tender bounty of their yielding beauty with all the hunger of our limitless desire, taste the pure and wholesome liquors of their tongues, and feed on the red-rose ripeness of their mouths all night long. Then, having taken and possessed, we shall be conquered by their dear surrender and lie, all through the brooding mystery of lilac dark and great-starred night, engulfed in the huge domain of their love, surrounded by the infinite, fertile, and all-taking earth clasp of their lavish bodies, bedded upon the silken swelling unction, the insatiate tenderness, the soft-withdrawing, and slow-yielding undulations of their velvet bellies!

"Oh, there are women in the West!" cried Garfield, Arthur, Harrison and Hayes, "and some day we shall find them standing at evening, waiting, in their doors. And we shall leave them in the morning, and hear them singing in their low sweet voices a song far, sorrowful, and golden, that tells of wandering and return. And we shall always know that we will find them there at evening when we come again!" they cried.]

And as Garfield, Arthur, Harrison and Hayes prowled softly up and down in the dark cobbled streets of sleeping towns, hearing the sudden shrill departure of the whistle in the night, the great wheels pounding at the river's edge, feeling the lilac dark, the heart beats of the sleeping men, and the attentive silence, the terror, savagery, and exultant joy, the huge mystery and promise of the immense and silent earth, did they not say:

"There are ten thousand lonely little towns at night, ten thousand lonely little towns of sleeping men, and we shall come to them forever in the night. We shall come to them like storm and fury, and a wild demonic impulse of exultant joy, dropping suddenly upon them from the fast express at night – leaving the train in darkness, in the dark mid-watches of the night, and being left then to the sudden silence, mystery and promise of an unknown little town. Oh, we shall come to them forever in the night," they cried, "in winter among howling winds and swirling snow. Then we shall make our tracks along the sheeted fleecy whiteness of an empty silent little street, and find our door at length, and know the instant that we come to it that it is ours. And we shall knock upon it then," they cried, "and find her waiting for us in the storm-white silence of the night, in the huge unknown mystery, magic, savage joy and promise of America. Then we shall stay with her in darkness while storm beats about the house and the white mounting drifts of swirling snow engulf us. We shall see the flower-whiteness of her face below us, the night-time darkness of her cloud of hair across our arm, and know all the mystery, tenderness and surrender of her white-dark beauty, her fragrant whiteness and slow sensual undulance. And we shall stay with her while storm howls about the house," they said, "and the huge drifts rise about us. And we shall leave her in the whitened silence of the morning, and hear her whisper of farewell, and always know that she will be there waiting for us when storms howl at night, and we drop off the fast express, and come to find her through the swirling snow, leaving our footprints on the whitened, empty, silent streets of unknown little towns, lost at the heart of storm and darkness upon the lonely, wild, and all-exultant mystery of the everlasting earth and of America."

Then, had Garfield, Arthur, Harrison and Hayes not said as they waited there in lilac darkness in the barren cobbled street [before the lavish lighted promise of the brothel]: "Oh, there are women in the South with dark eyes and the white magnolia faces. They are moving beneath the droop of old mossed trees in darkness in the sorrowful haunting tree-barred levels of the South. Now they are moving on the sweep of ancient lawns, moving beside the great slow-flowing rivers in the night! Their step is light and soundless as the dark, they drift the white ghost-glimmer of their beauty under ancient trees, their words are soft and slow and hushed, and sweeter far than honey, and suddenly their low and tender laugh, slow, swelling, rich, and sensual, comes welling from the great vat of the dark. The perfume of their slow white flesh is flower-sweet, magnolia-strange, and filled with all the secret languors of desire! Oh, there are secret women in the South!" they cried, "who drift like phantoms under drooping trees at night the sensual, secret languor of their loveliness, and the great slow rivers of the South are flowing by them, and the slow perfume, the mystery, the death, the terror, the evil and the sorrow of the Southern night is waiting all around them in the brooding mystery of all its fathomless fecundity, the thick jungle voice and fragrance of its million-noted ululation. Oh, there are secret, sensual women in the South," they cried, "who move by darkness under drooping trees in the white ghost-glimmer of their magnolia loveliness, and we shall find them!

"And there are women in the North," cried Garfield, Arthur, Harrison and Hayes, "who wait for us with Viking eyes, the deep breast and the great limbs of the Amazons. There are powerful and lovely women in the North," they said, "whose eyes are blue and depthless as a mountain lake. Their glorious hair is braided into ropes of ripened grain, and their names are Lundquist, Neilsen, Svensen, Jorgensen, and Brandt. They are waiting for us in the wheat-fields of the North, they are waiting for us at the edges of the plains, they are waiting for us in the forests of great trees. Their eyes are true and level, and their great hearts are the purest and most faithful on the earth, and they will wait for us until we come to them. [Then they will clasp us in a hug of bear-like tenderness, engulf us in the cradle of their mighty limbs, and break our backs with the powerful and sweet submissions of their infinite surrender] and be forever faithful to us."

And finally did not Garfield, Arthur, Harrison and Hayes, those fierce and jubilant young men, who waited there, as we have waited, in the silent barren street [before the brothel] with trembling lips, numb hands, with terror, savage joy, exultant wildness alive and stirring in their entrails – did they not feel, as we have felt, when they heard the shrill departing warning of the whistle in the lilac dark, the sound of great wheels pounding at the river's edge? Did they not feel, as we have felt, as they waited there in all the intolerable sweetness, wildness, mystery and terror of the great earth in the month of April, and knew themselves alone, alive, and young and mad with secret desire and hunger in all the sleeping silence of the night, the huge impending, cruel, all-promise of this land? Were they not torn, as we were, by sharp pain and wordless lust, the asp of time, the thorn of spring, the sharp, the tongueless cry? Did they not say:

"Oh, there are women in the East – and new lands, morning, and a shining city! There are forgotten fume-flaws of bright smoke above Manhattan, the forest of masts about the crowded isle, the proud cleavages of departing ships, the soaring web, the wing-like swoop and joy of the great bridge, and men with derby hats who come across the bridge to greet us – come, brothers, let us go to find them all! For the huge murmur of the city's million-footed life, far, bee-like, drowsy, strange as time, has come to haunt our ears with all its golden prophesy of joy and triumph, fortune, happiness, and love such as no men before have ever known.

"Oh, brothers, in the city, in the far-shining glorious time-enchanted spell of that enfabled city we shall find great men and lovely women, and unceasingly ten thousand new delights, a thousand magical adventures! We shall wake at morning in our rooms of lavish house to hear the hoof and wheel upon the city street again, and smell the harbor, fresh, half-rotten, with its bracelet of bright tides, its traffic of proud sea-borne ships, its purity and joy of dancing morning-gold – and feel, with an unspeakable sorrow and delight, that there are ships there, there are ships – and something in our hearts we cannot utter.

"And we shall smell the excellent sultry fragrance of boiling coffee, and know the sensual luxuries of walnut chambers in whose shuttered amber morning-light proud beauties slowly stir in drowsy warmth their lavish limbs. Then we shall smell, with the sharp relish of our awakened hunger the exultant breakfast smells: the pungent bacon, crisping to a turn, the grilled kidneys, eggs, and sausages, and the fragrant stacks of gold-brown wheat cakes smoking hot. Then we shall move, alive and strong and full of hope, through all the swarming lanes of morning and know the good green smell of money, the heavy leathers and the sumptuous walnut of great merchants, the power, the joy, the certitude and ease of proud success. We shall come at furious noon to slake our thirst with drinks of rare and subtle potency in sumptuous bars of swart mahogany in the good fellowship of men, the spicey fragrance of the lemon rind, and Angostura bitters. Then, hunger whetted, pulse aglow and leaping with the sharp spur of our awakened appetite, we shall eat from the snowy linen of the greatest restaurants in the world. We shall be suavely served and tenderly cared for by the pious unction of devoted waiters. We shall be quenched with old wine and fed with the rare and priceless honesty, the maddening

Rutherford B. Hayes,
nineteenth president of the United States.
Courtesy of the Library of Congress

succulence of grand familiar food and noble cooking, fit to match the peerless relish of our hunger!

"Street of the day, with the unceasing promise of your million-footed life, we come to you!" they cried. "Streets of the thunderous wheels at noon, streets of the great parades of marching men, the bands' bright oncoming blare, the brave stick-candy whippings of a flag, street of the cries and shouts, the swarming feet, the man-swarm ever passing in its million-footed weft – street of the jounting cabs, the ringing hooves, the horse cars and the jingling bells, the in-horse ever bending its sad nodding head towards its lean and patient comrade on the right – great street of furious life and movement, noon, and joyful labors, your image blazes in our hearts forever, and we come!

"Street of the morning, street of hope!" they cried. "Street of coolness, slanted light, the frontal cliff and gulch of steep blue shade, street of the dancing morning-gold of waters on the flashing tides, street of the smell of rusty weathered slips, the blunt-nosed ferry foaming in with its packed wall of small white staring faces, all silent and intent, all turned toward *you* – proud street! Street of the exultant sultry smells of new-ground coffee, the good green smell of money, the fresh half-rotten harbor smells with all its evocation of your mast-bound harbor and its tide of ships, great street! – Street of the old buildings grimed richly with the warm and mellow dinginess of trade – street of the million morning feet forever hurrying onward in the same direction – proud street of hope and joy and morning, in your steep canyon we shall win the wealth, the fame, the power and the esteem which our lives and talents merit!

"Street of the night!" they cried, "great street of mystery and suspense, terror and delight, eagerness and hope, street edged forever with the dark menace of impending joy, an unutterable happiness and fulfilment, street of gaiety, warmth, and evil, street of the great hotels, the lavish bars and restaurants, and the softly-golden glow, the fading lights and empetalled whiteness of a thousand hushed white thirsty faces in the crowded theatres, street of the tidal flood of faces, lighted with your million lights and all thronging, tireless and unquenched in their insatiate searching after pleasure, street of the lovers coming along with slow steps, their faces turned towards each other, lost in the oblivion of love among the everlasting web and weaving of the crowd, street of the white face, the painted mouth, the shining and inviting eye, the slow proud pacings of the whores in darkness – O street of night, with all your mystery, joy, and terror – we have thought of you, proud street.

"And we shall move at evening in the noiseless depths of sumptuous carpets through all the gaiety, warmth, and brilliant happiness of great lighted chambers of the night, filled with the mellow thrum and languor of the violins, and where the loveliest and most desirable women in the world – the beloved daughters of great merchants, bankers, millionaires, or rich young widows, beautiful, loving, and alone – are moving with a slow proud undulance, a look of depthless tenderness in their fragile, lovely faces. And the loveliest of them all," they cried, "is ours, is ours forever, if we want her! For, brothers, in the city, in the far-shining, magic, golden city we shall move among great men and glorious women and know nothing but strong joy and happiness forever, winning by our courage, talent, and deserving the highest and most honored place in the most fortunate and happy life that men have ever known, if only we will go and make it ours!"

So, thinking, feeling, waiting as we have waited in the sleeping silence of the night in silent streets [before the shuttered windows of the brothel], hearing as we have heard, the sharp blast of the warning whistle, the thunder of great wheels upon the river's edge, feeling, as we have felt, the mystery of night time and of April, the huge impending presence, the wild and secret promise, of the savage, lonely, everlasting earth, finding, as we have found, no doors to enter, and being torn, as we were torn, by the thorn of spring, the sharp, the wordless cry, did they not carry – these young men of the past, Garfield, Arthur, Harrison and Hayes – even as we have carried, within those little tenements of bone, blood, sinew, sweat and agony, the intolerable burden of all the pain, joy, hope and savage hunger that a man can suffer, that the world can know?

"Were they not lost? Were they not lost, as all of us have been, who have known youth and hunger in this land, and who have waited lean and mad and lonely in the night, and who have found no goal, no wall, no ending, and no door?

"The years flow by like water and one day it is spring again. Brothers, shall we ever ride out of the gates of the East again, as we did once at morning, and seek again, as we did then, new lands, the promise of the war, and glory, joy, and triumph, and a shining city?

"O youth, still wounded, living, feeling with a woe unutterable, still grieving with a grief intolerable, still thirsting with a thirst unquenchable – where are we to seek? For the wild tempest breaks above us, the wild fury beats about us, the wild hunger feeds upon us – and we are houseless, doorless, unassuaged, and driven on forever; and our brains are mad, our hearts are wild and wordless, and we cannot speak."

■

The Bank Failure

The bank failure is foreshadowed in a paragraph cut from the typescript by Wolfe: see p. 15, ll. 17–21.

Now I could hear my father's voice upon the porch again, the premonitory scraping of the boarders' chairs, the sound of people going down the leafy street towards home, a sense of coolness, silence, the huge sweet tides of oncoming all-engulfing sleep. Suddenly, coming down the darkened street I heard the fat short thring of a bicycle bell, the hum of the light wired wheels: the little winking light curved over sharply as it neared the house, slowed down and stopped.

The boy got off, lifted the wheel, kicked down the pedal deftly till it balanced on the curb, and then came quickly up the concrete steps across the walk and up onto the porch, bringing to us all the unknown thrill and hope and menace of that little slip of yellow magic called a telegram. The voices on the porch stopped instantly: in a moment I could hear my father saying sharply, "Who? Hey?" and then Mr. Helm saying in an excited tone, "Vas? Who? . . . For me?"

His chair scraped heavily, he got up, and lumbered rapidly across the porch, saying in an excited, rather bewildered tone:

"Ja. . . . Vait a minute. . . . I vill sign. . . . Gif us some light!" he cried. Someone switched the porch-light on, and then I could hear Mr. Helm breathing heavily as he scrawled his name down in the messenger's book. The boy ran down the steps, across the walk, and in a moment had got on his wheel again, and with a thring of bells was coasting swiftly off downhill.

Then for a moment there was a heavy breathing silence, a rattling of the flimsy paper as he tore the message open, and then heavy, breathy, and attentive silence once again.

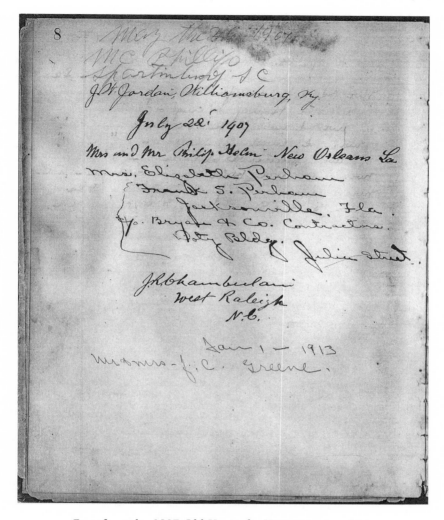

Page from the 1907 Old Kentucky Home guest register,
signed by Mrs. and Mr. Helm.
Courtesy of the Thomas Wolfe Memorial, Asheville, N.C.

Suddenly, Mr. Helm cried out in a hoarse bewildered tone:
"Else! . . . Else! . . . Komm' hier! . . . Schnell! . . . Um Gottes willen!
. . . Was soll dies sein!"

I could hear the old woman speak to him in an excited tone, get up,
and waddle toward him, and almost immediately there was a choking,
gasping noise, and the sound of something heavy falling to the porch.

When I got there, the boarders were all on their feet, staring with star-tled faces at the old man, who was sitting stupidly on the floor, upright and stolid, with his short heavy legs thrust straight out before him. My father and McKeithan were bending over him on either side, they got their hands beneath his heavy shoulders and began to lift him up, and all the time the old man's heavy arms were stretched out in their grasp with a kind of terrible paralyzed passivity, and as they lifted them, his ponderous bullet head rolled slowly from side to side, and he looked stupidly and vacantly at them as if he had never seen them before, and had no notion where he was.

There was something at once horribly comic and tragic in his posture and in the vacant stupid looks he gave my father and McKeithan: I have never seen men shot in battle but I am certain that a man struck by a shell might look at the people around him in the same stupid foolish way that old man Helm looked at my father.

Even when they had lifted him he still held clutched in one pudgy old hand the crumpled telegram. My father took it from his hand and read it. The telegram bore the news that the bank had closed its doors, that a ruinous deficit had been discovered, and that the president had fled, tak-ing with him a huge sum of money. The bank, in fact, had been looted down to the last buck in the vault, although old Mr. Helm did not know it at that moment. Mr. Helm's beloved president fled to South America and was never captured, thousands of depositors were ruined, and Mr. Helm himself, who departed the next day with his wife for New Orleans, lost not only pension and savings, but the modest investment of a lifetime's labor.

He died four months later, and death was merciful, for he was a para-lyzed gibbering idiot of a man when death released him.

That was the year the war came. And war brings death to men as well as life. To the old man it brings ruin, heart-break, hopelessness, and death. But to the young man it impends forever like a glorious and exultant prophesy in every blade and leaf and flower, in a woman's laughter in the dark, and the all-enfolding mystery of velvet-breasted night. It fills his heart with thoughts of glory and exultant joy, with haunting memories of old time, and the lost voices and forgotten faces of his father's youth. And it comes to him like madness in the night, whispering its dark and secret promises of fame, the fellowship of heroes, the love of glorious women, with flight and darkness, morning, and the earth.

The Manuscripts and Typescripts

The archive of Thomas Wolfe's papers donated by William B. Wisdom to the Houghton Library at Harvard University includes nearly 800 pages of manuscript (holograph) and 240 of typescript (or carbon copy) identified or recognizable in the catalogue notations as the short story or novelette "The Four Lost Men." (All the material—see below—with catalogue numbers in the 600s have the heading "[The hills beyond Pentland]"; "(708)" and "(709)" are headed "[The four lost men].") The material is catalogued by number and folder, each folder in the archive holding fifteen sheets (though not invariably fifteen). Consecutive folders and pages within folders are not always in order; that is inevitable where there are hundreds of unnumbered, loose pages.

Wolfe, who did not himself type, sometimes entered page numbers by hand at the tops of typed pages, but manuscript pages are unnumbered. His habit was to write on one side of each sheet of unlined typewriter paper; sometimes he used the clean versos of pages that already had a line or two of typed or holograph material. He did not erase, but made corrections by crossing out words or sentences and adding interlinear material; occasionally, most of a page must be read in alternating lines.

The typing was done by a professional (or professionals) remarkably adept at reading Wolfe's handwriting, who sometimes used a device, probably a tape, that could generate typed copies from different appropriately equipped machines: much of the typed material exists in copies that are not carbon copies. Errors, line endings, underlinings, typed x-ing outs, and typed corrections are identical, but the type sizes are, for different copies of otherwise identical material, both pica and elite. Such deviations are ignored in the descriptions that follow; only variant typings are specified.

The ordering below is that of the Houghton catalogue. The term "manuscript" is used for holograph material and "typescript" for material that is not holograph. ("Typescript" includes ribbon, carbon, and tape-generated copies.) Page numbers preceded by "p." or "pp." locate the material in the edition in hand.

Manuscript

(664) *folders 1–5*: 66 pages about boardinghouse visitors from New Orleans, concentrating on the Irish as a group and individually on George O'Ryan, a remembered contemporary of the narrator. None of this material appears in any version of "The Four Lost Men," but the paragraph beginning "The others had long since left us . . ." on p. 8 suggests a connection.

(664) *folders 5–9*: 56 pages concerning the Civil War at Gettysburg. (The sounds of distant guns, the farm family's industry, and the character of the matriarch are related to the *O Lost* prologue, unpublished until 2000.) This manuscript material, though not used in "The Four Lost Men," is reflected in the paragraph that follows the space break on p. 26.

(664) *folders 9–20*: nearly 180 pages of manuscript material related to the station platform scene that begins *Of Time and the River.* There is no apparent connection to "The Four Lost Men."

(664) *folders 20–25*: 68 pages that conclude "The Four Lost Men"— from "Did they not, as we, when young . . ." on p. 42 to the final words, ". . . we cannot speak."

(664) *folders 25–29*: 60 pages that conform to "The Four Lost Men" from the beginning of the story ("Suddenly, at the green heart . . .") through ". . . attentive silence as my father talked." on p. 5, and "He spoke of all the wars and troubles . . ." on p. 26 through ". . . And they were lost." on p. 39—except that none of the material treating the boarders Helm and McKeithan appears. The *Scribner's* magazine short-story text follows this manuscript segment closely.

(664) *folders 29–31*: another 32 pages of station platform *Of Time and the River* material.

(664) *folders 31–32*: 15 pages of "The Four Lost Men" text: "From time to time . . ." (p. 6) through ". . . of a child." (p. 8).

(664) *folders 32–34*: 30 pages treating boardinghouse visitor Norah Ryan, from Pittsburgh.

(665) folders 1–2: 25 additional pages about Norah Ryan, with rumors of her association with the death of Herman Rosenthal. There are allusions to "Gyp the Blood," "Lefty Louie," "Dago Frank," and "Whitey Lewis" (who were executed for the 1914 murder of Rosenthal). This and the catalogue entry immediately above have no apparent connection to "The Four Lost Men."

(665) folders 2–12: 146 pages of "The Four Lost Men" text, from "The others had long since left us. . . . " (p. 8) to the space break on p. 26.

(665) folders 12–18: 90 pages of "The Four Lost Men" text; 81 pages of folders 12–17 begin "'Controversy, was it?' . . ." (p. 27) and end ". . . had gone from him forever." (p. 38), with the omission of "He was a man in his late thirties . . ." (p. 28) through ". . . the cause or remedy himself." (p. 29), which appears separately on the last 4 pages of folder 17 and the first 5 of folder 18. [5 pages of manuscript material beginning "'In 1884,' he said, 'I cast my vote for James G. Blaine . . .'" (p. 35) from (664) folders 28–29, above, overlap with manuscript material here. The *Scribner's* magazine story conforms to the much shorter (664) version.]

(665) folders 18–19: 17 pages omitted from "The Four Lost Men." Mr. Helm is with the others on the boardinghouse porch when he receives the telegram informing him of the failure of his beloved New Orleans bank. The episode, included here as "The Bank Failure," was written for "The Four Lost Men"; the last paragraph reconnects with the "present" of impending war.

Note that there is no manuscript here for the material "Therefore, even in his death . . ." (p. 19) through ". . . and would not die." (p. 20) and "For who was Garfield, martyred man . . ." (p. 39) through ". . . single wordless cry" (p. 42).

Typescript

(677) folders 1–4: 51 pages as follows: (A) Pages 7 through 22 and 31 through 34, so numbered but not in Wolfe's hand, are identical to the similarly numbered pages in (708) folders 1–5 (referred to hereinafter as "our copy-text"). The pages are also numbered 1 through 20, apparently in the same editorial hand. Three pages of typescript that conform to manuscript (665) folders 18–19 (Mr. Helm receiving the telegram) are paginated 21–23, and there are editorial markings indicating an attempt to have them follow the paragraph that ends ". . . and smoked" on p. 25. These

three pages are also paginated 55–57, not by Wolfe, and 72–74 in Wolfe's hand. (B) 22 pages—unpaginated and unmarked except for a holograph X at the top of the first page—are identical to the corresponding pages 7–28 of our copy-text. (C) There are two additional copies (unmarked) of the three-page typescript corresponding to (665) folders 18–19.

(678) *folders 1–2:* 26 pages about boardinghouse visitors from New Orleans. It is not part of "The Four Lost Men," but Mr. and Mrs. Helm are described. The last 6 pages of folder 2 correspond to manuscript (664) folders 1–3.

(678) *folders 2–4:* 26 pages of incomplete typescript corresponding to pages 29–54 of our copy-text ("It will be found . . ."—p. 22—through "And they were lost. / * * * * * * *"—p. 39).

(678) *folders 5–6:* 25 pages duplicating (678) folders 1–2, above, except that the first page is missing.

(678) *folders 6–7:* 26 pages duplicating (678) folders 2–4. The pages are hand numbered (29–54) and lightly marked with brackets and lines indicating deletions, probably by Wolfe.

(679) *folders 1–2:* 26 pages, the second 13 duplicating the first 13. In each case, the first three (unnumbered) pages are like the text of the *Scribner's* magazine story from "soon!" (p. 89) through ". . . mystery of the earth." (p. 91), except that forty words are omitted or altered in the magazine text. The fourth (unnumbered) page begins in the middle of a paragraph the ending of which ("For who saw Garfield in the streets . . . which was which?") resembles both a *From Death to Morning* paragraph (p. 78) and a paragraph of our copy-text (p. 39). From line 9 of the fourth page ("Had Garfield, Arthur, Harrison and Hayes ever been young?") through the end of the thirteenth (unnumbered) page (". . . wordless cry, did they not?"), the text differs very little from our copy-text, p. 42 through p. 51. The typing, however, is different.

(708) *folders 1–5:* 71 pages; this is a nearly complete typescript of the long version of "The Four Lost Men"—with holograph corrections and emendations by Wolfe—and is our copy-text for this edition, with 5 pages inserted. There are two typed title pages. The first reads "Part I / The Hound Of Darkness / Book / America Unvisited / THE FOUR LOST MEN" with "From Death to Morning," "(1793–1916)," and other notations added in a hand that is not Wolfe's. The second title page reads "THE WAR IN APRIL / By / Thomas Wolfe"; everything except "THE" is crossed out, and "Four Lost Men" is substituted by Wolfe. The pages of text are

numbered by hand, probably Wolfe's, 1–72. Page 22 is missing, and pages 31, 32, 33, and 34 are missing. The text for page 22 ("leathery-looking ear, from . . . . shadow of his former self, his" pp. 17–18) is supplied from typescript (677). Pages 31, 32, 33, and 34 ("its color, was . . ."—p. 23—through ". . . ven Hayes vas Bresident . . . . "—p. 25) are supplied from typescript (678) folders 2–4.

(708) *folders* 6–7: 23 pages duplicating our copy-text, with the omission of pages 7–54 ("The three boarders who dared . . ."—p. 7—through "And they were lost. / ∗ ∗ ∗ ∗ ∗ ∗ ∗"—p. 39). There is a title page that duplicates the second title page of our copy-text, also with Wolfe's holograph revision. He wrote "0 –46" at the top of the title page and "0 45 G.A.H.&H" at the top of page 55. Except for the substitution of one word ("the" for "low" on page 4—p. 4, l. 5), the (unpaginated) sheets are unmarked.

(709): there is one folder; its cover sheet specifies "14 s. (14p.)." Ordered A–N, they are as follows. A: a duplicate of page 66 of our copy-text ("sweeter far than honey . . . until we come to them."—p. 47); there are a few deletions marked, and Wolfe wrote "The <u>Hills Beyond Pentland</u>—Garfield Arthur H and H" across the top of the page. B: a duplicate of our copy-text page 58 ("the dead Americans . . . plain tremendous poetry"—pp. 41–42); the first three lines have been crossed out with typed Xs, and the word "three" is emended to "six" in Wolfe's hand. C: An unmarked typed page that is not part of our copy-text; the three lines that were deleted from sheet B are at the top of the page, followed by three paragraphs used in the *From Death to Morning* text, "As we leaned . . . no speech."—p. 80. D: an unmarked duplicate of page 6 of our copy-text ("or agreement, and then . . . full swing again."—pp. 5–6). E: another typed version, slightly abridged ("'Ah, Lord!' my father said . . . And they were lost / ∗ ∗ ∗ ∗ ∗ ∗"), of most of page 54 of our copy-text; this text was used in *From Death to Morning*—pp. 77–78. F–H: an untitled three-page short story about a train engineer whose life is fulfilled by decades of the daily waves of a stranger and her daughter; the story, unrelated to "The Four Lost Men," is "The Far and the Near" in *From Death to Morning*, except that (1) sentences that connect the story to the imagination of a (third-person) observer are cut from "The Far and the Near," and (2) the conventional short-story denouement (retired, the engineer visits the house and meets the women) is not part of the untitled typescript. J, I (in that order): the typing is not that of our copy-text; the (shorter) text is that of the *From*

Death to Morning version ("James Buchanan's time – for I was . . . silence and the boarders waited." — pp. 75–77. K: the typing is different, but the text varies little from that of our copy-text ("'Ah – hah,' said McKeithan . . . while she could." — pp. 35–36); in K, four lines that are omitted in our copy-text follow the word "could." L: one page that begins like our copy-text page 39 ("election after he'd . . ." — p. 28) continues through ". . . even as he laughed."; but L omits two pages of typescript to continue with "Now I could hear his right foot . . ." (p. 30) and ends, like our copy-text page 41, with ". . . through the brain, dying" (p. 30); the manuscript for the omitted material was written separately; see (665) folders 17–18, above. M and N are duplicate copies of K and L. Pages I through L are unmarked except that each has an X drawn across it. Wolfe sometimes marked pages in this way to indicate that he no longer needed them.

A.B.

■

Textual Notes

Page/line numbers in the left-hand column refer to the edition in hand. The word or passage immediately following is the reading in this edition. (A pair of brackets means that the material within them was crossed out by Thomas Wolfe.) The set of letters that follows gives the source of the reading in this edition; the single bracket points—or is open—in the direction of that reading. The single bracket is followed by the rejected reading or readings, their sources being indicated by the letter groups immediately to their right. Editorial explanation, where necessary, is in italics at the end of the entry.

TS is the copy-text typescript. MS is the corresponding manuscript. SM is the February 1934 issue of *Scribner's* magazine. *FDTM* is the 1935 short-story collection *From Death to Morning*. TSEdH identifies an emendation of the typescript made by an unknown editor, the hand not being Thomas Wolfe's; TSTWH, an emendation in Wolfe's hand. Ed means that the emendation was made by the editors of this edition.

There are editorial words, all in italics, throughout the textual notes. If they are not enclosed in parentheses, they identify or describe the designation that follows them. Thus:

"xxvii.2–3 [By / Thomas Wolfe] TS *brackets* Ed] *deleted* TSTWH" means that the brackets are supplied by "Ed," the editors of this edition; "By / Thomas Wolfe" is the typescript reading, but the words were deleted by Wolfe, "TSTWH."

If the italicized editorial words are within parentheses, they identify or describe the designation that immediately precedes them. Thus:

"4.5 . . . TSEdH (*duplicate page*), SM, FDTM" means that the emended reading was made in a duplicate page of typescript in a hand other than

Wolfe's. "8.9 prophecy Ed, MS *(probable)*" means that the manuscript reading was probably "prophecy," but not so distinctly as to be accepted as the source of the emendation.

xxvii.2–3	[By / Thomas Wolfe] TS *brackets* Ed] *deleted* TSTWH
1.2	night, I heard my father's voice again. That year I was TS, MS, SM, FDTM] night, he heard his father's voice again. That year he was TSTWH. *Wolfe's emendation of TS from first to third person ceases after the second sentence.*
1.2–3	sixteen, [the week before I had come home from my first year at college,] and TS, MS *brackets* Ed] sixteen, and TSTWH
1.17	tight-folded Ed] light folded TS, SM, FDTM. *The MS reading "light" uncertain because Wolfe did not consistently cross the letter "t."*
2.21	gusting MS] gusty TS, SM, FDTM
4.5	heard the rich TSEdH *(duplicate page)*, SM, FDTM] heard low rich TS, MS
4.11	wizardry MS, SM, *FDTM*] wizardy TS
7.8	his assistant TSTWH] his chief assistant TS, MS
7.15	strange golden TSTWH] strange deep golden TS, MS
8.9	prophecy Ed, MS *(probable)*] prophesy TS
10.24	sorrow. They MS] sorrow, they TS
10.30	acceptance. We Ed, MS *(probable)*] acceptance, we TS
10.32	lived most lonely Stet MS, TS
11.11	intimate MS] intricate TS
11.34–12.14	forever. ¶ [The feeling. . . . Me.] ¶ This TS, MS *brackets* Ed] forever. ¶ This TSTWH
12.31	prophecies Ed] prophesies TS, MS
13.17	Hesperides MS] Hesperdes TS. *See explanatory note.*
13.21–26	joy? ¶ [It was. . . . ground.] It was TS, MS *brackets* Ed] joy? ¶ It was TSTWH
13.36	lilac dark, a TSTWH] lilac, a TS. *The MS passage varies in word order, but Wolfe accepted the typist's error, adding the word "dark" so that the TS would make sense.*
14.16–17	free-handed TSTWH, MS] free-headed TS
14.18–19	Orleans." / * * * * / ¶ And TSTWH] Orleans." ¶ And TS, MS
14.27	prophecies Ed, MS *(probable)*] prophesies TS

15.16–22	him. ¶ [For even. . . . it.] ¶ A German TS, MS *brackets* Ed] him. ¶ A German TSTWH
15.22	birth, Mr. Helm had TSTWH] birth, he had TS, MS
16.5	boundless TSTWH, MS *(probable)*] bondless TS
16.10	unbounded TSTWH, MS *(probable)*] unbonded TS
16.36	Nod my chob! Ed] Not my yob! TS, MS. *Mr. Helm's pronunciation has been made consistent.*
17.10	Den Ed] Then TS, MS
19.2	the lost MS] that lost TS
19.24	minds Ed] mind TS. *There is no MS for 46.9–51.1.*
19.38	unescapable Stet TS
21.14	death MS] time TS
22.13	mothers' Ed] mother's TS, MS
22.14	These MS] There TS
22.18	known MS] know TS
22.30	barytones Stet TS, MS
23.7	more MS] most TS
24.20	on MS] in TS
24.20	employes Stet TS, MS. *Wolfe makes a now-old-fashioned distinction between this masculine plural noun and the feminine, "employees."*
24.29	come Ed, MS *(probable)*] came TS
24.33	chust Ed] yust TS, MS
25.4	vorked MS] worked TS
25.16	odders Ed] others TS, MS
25.31	und Ed] and TS
25.32	vell MS] well TS
25.34	it vas MS] it was TS
26.22	spoke Ed] spoken TS. *The phrase* my father spoke then of *is omitted in MS;* SM *and* FDTM *follow MS omission.*
27.7	imprecisely Ed] unprecisely TS; illogically MS, *SM, FDTM*
27.8	his MS, SM, *FDTM*] he TS
28.1	*that* MS *(underlined)*] that TS
28.14	iss Ed] is TS, MS
28.14	righd MS] right TS
28.34	jangled MS] jungled TS
29.36	drowning, and though MS] drowning, though TS
30.8	for TSEdH *(duplicate page)*] of MS, TS
32.35	breast MS] heart TS

33.20	silently and slightly MS] slightly and slightly MS *(emended)*; strongly and slightly TS
34.10	tone of almost MS] tone almost TS
36.35	iss Ed] is TS, MS
37.5	spat Ed, MS *(probable)*] spit TS
38.8	thinly MS] thinking TS
39.33–34	loitering up Stet TS, SM, FDTM. *There is no MS for 104.11–113.12.*
40.10; 42.8	Wilson's Creek Ed] Wilson's Mill TS, SM, FDTM. *See explanatory note.*
40.10	Spangler's Spring Ed] Spangler's Run TS, SM, FDTM. *See explanatory note.*
40.25	William Gilmore Simms Ed] William Gillmore Sims TS, SM, FDTM
40.37; 41.15	sallows Stet. *Both TS occurrences exhibit unusual and careful overtyping, suggesting consultation by an uncertain typist.* SM *prints "sallows" once and "shallows" once;* FDTM *emends* SM *"sallows" (104.II.34) to "shallows" (124.12). The Oxford English Dictionary includes "sallows" with the meaning of "willows."*
41.6	hearts: *Three additional paragraphs follow here in both the* SM *and* FDTM *texts. See* FDTM*, p. 80.*
41.9	six TSTWH *(duplicate page)*] three TS
42.2	O plain, O Ed] Oh, plain, oh- TS; You plain, oh- SM, FDTM
42.8	Creek Ed] Mills TS; Mill SM, FDTM. *See 40.10.*
42.9	O you TS] you SM, FDTM
42.13	O proud Ed] oh proud TS; oh, proud SM, FDTM
42.19	*after break* ¶ [Hearing my father's voice then on the porch, I thought:] had TS *brackets* Ed] ¶ Had TSTWH
42.28–29	down the doorless avenues of night TSTWH] down past brothels in the dark hours of the night TS, MS; down in the dark hours of the night SM, FDTM. *Wolfe was persuaded by Perkins to remove the references to the Presidents as brothel-frequenters for the* SM *text (Wolfe to Alfred Dashiell, late 1933: To Loot My Life Clean, p. 123).*
42.32	jounting Stet TS, SM, FDTM; rattling MS
43.12–13	and April TSTWH] and of April TS, MS; in April SM, FDTM
45.1	a house, proud, evil, lavish, lighted TSTWH, SM, FDTM

] the whorehouse, proud, evil, lavish, lighted TS; proud, evil, lavish, lighted brothels MS

45.5   darkness TSTWH, *SM, FDTM*] street before the brothel TS, MS

45.10–11   them. [Coming . . . eyes.] They TS, MS *brackets* Ed] them. They TSTWH

45.17–36   evening! [Then. . . . cried.] ¶ And TS *brackets* Ed] evening. ¶ And TSTWH. *The MS for this passage varies too much to have been the immediate source of the copy-text TS. Wolfe probably made emendations in now-missing pages of typescript. There is a thirteen-page type-script segment ("(679) folder 1") that corresponds to the MS, but it is unrevised. MS [TS variations are as follows:* And [45.17 Then; tender fragrant [45.19 fragrant; lavish empire [45.20 tender bounty; feed on the sweet red ripeness of their mouths, and taste the pure and whole-some liquors of their tongues and [45.21–23 taste the. . . . Then; slow-yielding all-receiving and all-tender undu-lance of [45.28–29 slow-yielding undulations of; singing in the house, and always know [45.33 singing in their. . . . shall always know

45.37   streets of sleeping towns, TSTWH] street before the brothel TS, MS

46.7   fast TSTWH, MS] vast TS

46.15   waiting for TSTWH] waiting, waiting for MS, TS

46.17   stay TSTWH] lie TS, MS

46.20   mystery, tenderness TSTWH] mystery, voluptuous ten-derness TS, MS

46.21   her fragrant TSTWH] the fragrant TS, MS

46.21   and slow TSTWH] and the slow TS, MS

46.22   undulance. And TSTWH] undulance of her lavish body. And TS, MS

46.30   earth and of America MS] earth of America TS

46.32–33   street [before the lavish lighted promise of the brothel]: "Oh TS *brackets* Ed] street: "Oh TSTWH; street before the brothels: "oh MS

47.5   secret languors TSTWH] secret fatal languors TS, MS

47.13   trees in the Ed] trees the MS, TS

47.17   Amazons. There TSTWH] Amazons. Oh there TS, MS

47.24–27   them. [Then . . . surrender] TS, MS *brackets* Ed] them." TSTWH

47.27	and be forever faithful to us." ¶ And MS] ¶ And TS
47.30	street [before the brothel] with TS, MS *brackets* Ed] street, with TSTWH
47.31	stirring TSTWH, MS] strong TS
48.11–12	known. ¶ "Oh TSTWH] known. "Oh TS, MS, *SM, FDTM*
48.15	house MS] brown TS, *SM, FDTM*
48.20–21	utter. ¶ "And TSTWH] utter. And TS, MS
48.22	and know the TSTWH] and think of TS, MS
48.22	sensual luxuries TSTWH] sensual silken luxury TS, MS
48.23	in drowsy TSTWH] in sensual TS, MS
49.8	jounting Stet TS, MS, *SM, FDTM*
50.26	O street Ed] oh, street TS, *SM, FDTM*; oh street MS
50.33	widows MS, *SM, FDTM*] windows TS
51.5	streets [before the shuttered windows of the brothel], hearing TS, MS *brackets* Ed] streets, hearing TSTWH
51.13–15	carried, within those little tenements of bone, blood, sinew, sweat and agony, the intolerable burden of all the pain, joy, hope and savage hunger that a man can suffer, that the world can know? TSTWH, *SM, FDTM*] carried, the intolerable burden of their savage hunger into the kept and carnal nakedness of whores? TS, MS
51.23	war TSTWH, *SM, FDTM*] night TS, MS
51.23	city? Ed, *SM, FDTM*] city. TS, MS
52.23	breathy Ed, MS *(probable)*] breathing TS
54.21	buck MS] brick TS
54.25	pension and savings Ed] pension, savings MS, TS

Explanatory Notes

8.20   enchanted years of "1908" (See 11.22–23 golden world of "1908"): The meaning is obscure, but "1908" clearly had significance for Wolfe. MS 665, p. 14 in the "The Hills Beyond Pentland" material includes this reference to a boarder at the Old Kentucky Home:

> —Yes! I could fix a year, a month, a moment of dark time for that lost magic of the buried life, but nothing could evoke it better, in all its thousand hues and qualities of enchantment, than the strange sorcery which the figures "1908" came to have for me—and into which the memory of that lost golden girl would be forever woven.

Wolfe's eighth birthday was October 3, 1908.

8.35   counterjumpers: clerks in a shop.

13.17   Hesperides: In Greek mythology Hesperus's daughters guarded the golden apples in the garden on the Isles of the Blest at the western end of the earth; hence the islands were named for them.

14.13   "The Chocolate Soldier": The title song of a hit operetta with music by Oscar Straus and lyrics translated by Stanislaus Stange that opened on Broadway in 1910.

14.13   "Tammany": 1905 song with music by Gus Edwards and lyrics by Vincent Bryan.

14.13–14 "Has Anybody Here Seen Kelly?": 1909 song with music by W. J. McKenna and lyrics by C. W. Murphy and Will Letters.

14.14   "Love Me and the World Is Mine": 1906 song with music by Ernest R. Ball and lyrics by Dave Reed Jr.

17.35ff   With a dozen word changes and other necessary alterations (Eugene Gant not being a first-person narrator, and his father's

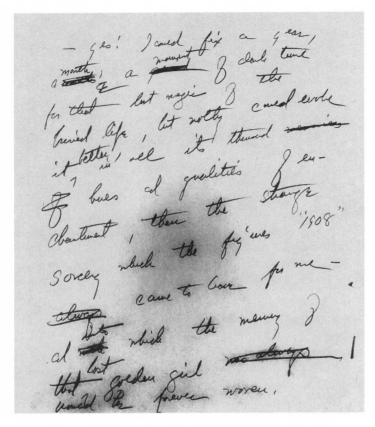

Manuscript page from "The Hills Beyond Pentland."
Courtesy of the Wisdom Collection, Houghton Library,
Harvard University

death having already happened), pages 271.12–273.37 in *Of
Time and the River* are taken directly from the long text of
"The Four Lost Men." There is re-ordering of paragraphs, as
follows: 17.35–19.14 ¶ Later, I . . . . powers. [*OT&R* 271.12–
272.9 ¶ Later, the boy . . . . powers.; 20.3–21.6 ¶ Now the
. . . . character. [*OT&R* 272.32–273.37 ¶ Now the . . . . character.; 21.7–28 ¶ Thus, one . . . . hands. [*OT&R* 272.10–31 ¶
Thus one . . . . hands.

   The untitled manuscript fragment (Thomas Wolfe Collec-
tion, Wilson Library, University of North Carolina, Chapel
Hill) edited by David Strange and published in facsimile as *My
Father's Hands* ([Bloomington, Ind.]: Thomas Wolfe Society,

2006) is a different composition.

26.24   Tartarian: pertaining to the area of central Asia east of the Caspian Sea.

26.25   Cipango: legendary island or islands east of Asia.

27.30   Hayes-Tilden controversy: The 1876 contest between Republican Rutherford B. Hayes, governor of Ohio, and Democrat Samuel Tilden, governor of New York, was the most controversial presidential election. Tilden won the popular vote by 254,235 votes and had 184 to Hayes's 165 Electoral College votes in the first report. Twenty votes were disputed: the returns from Oregon (one Electoral College vote), Florida (four), Louisiana (eight), and South Carolina (seven) were challenged by the Republicans. The bipartisan Electoral Commission established by Congress consisted of five senators, five representatives, and five Supreme Court justices. Seven of the members were to be Republicans and seven Democrats; the fifth justice was expected to be independent, but he voted with the Republicans. The commission voted eight to seven to award the election to Hayes by an Electoral College vote of 185–184. The voters' response to this result was bitter. It was alleged—probably correctly—that the contested Tilden totals in the three Southern states were altered as part of the deal to remove Federal troops from the former Confederate states.

35.10   Rum, Romanism, and Rebellion: In the 1884 Grover Cleveland–James G. Blaine presidential election, the Reverend Samuel D. Burchard, a supporter of Republican candidate Blaine, described the Democrats as the party of "Rum, Romanism, and Rebellion." Blaine's failure to disavow Burchard's statement purportedly cost him the Catholic vote and secured the presidency for Democrat Cleveland.

38.10   Garfield, Arthur, Harrison and Hayes: The order of these four presidencies was Hayes (1877–1881), Garfield (1881), Arthur (1881–1885), and Harrison (1889–1893). Wolfe's decision to alter the sequence of the presidents in his story was prompted by his ear.

39.4   Persepolis: ancient Persian city, site of palaces of kings.

39.15   felloe: "Felloe" means the rim of a wheel; hence "felloe-rim" is redundant.

40.10   Wilson's Creek: The battle at Wilson's Creek, Missouri, on 10 August 1861, resulted in a Confederate victory. No Ohio or Indiana units were involved. See textual note.

40.10   Spangler's Spring: part of the Battle of Gettysburg. On the third
          day of Gettysburg, 3 July 1863, the Twenty-Seventh Indiana
          and the Second Massachusetts charged the Confederate posi-
          tion near Culp's Hill with terrible Union casualties. Garfield,
          Harrison, and Hayes were not involved. See textual note.

40.25   Sir Walter Scott (1771–1832) and William Gilmore Simms
          (1806–1870): British and American authors of romantic histori-
          cal fiction.

45.19   Atlantean breasts: very large, oceanic. Not *Atalantean*.

48.4   fume-flaws: The meaning is obscure, but the *OED* provides
          "a detached piece of something" or "fragment" for "flaw"; thus
          "fume-flaws" may signify fragments of smoke or vapor.

49.9   in-horse: the left-side horse in a two-horse team.

■

The Four Lost Men
From Death to Morning *Version*

Suddenly, at the green heart of June, I heard my father's voice again. That year I was sixteen; the week before I had come home from my first year at college, and the huge thrill and menace of the war, which we had entered just two months before, had filled our hearts. And war gives life to men as well as death. It fills the hearts of young men with wild song and jubilation. It wells up in their throats in great-starred night, the savage cry of all their pain and joy. And it fills them with a wild and wordless prophecy not of death, but life, for it speaks to them of new lands, triumph, and discovery, of heroic deeds, the fame and fellowship of heroes, and the love of glorious unknown women—of a shining triumph and a grand success in a heroic world, and of a life more fortunate and happy than they have ever known.

So was it with us all that year. Over the immense and waiting earth, the single pulse and promise of the war impended. One felt it in the little towns at dawn, with all their quiet, casual, utterly familiar acts of life beginning. One felt it in the route-boy deftly flinging the light folded block of paper on a porch, a man in shirt-sleeves coming out upon the porch and bending for the paper, the slow-clopping hoofs of the milk horse in a quiet street, the bottle-clinking wagon, and the sudden pause, the rapid footsteps of the milkman and the clinking bottles, then clopping hoof and wheel, and morning, stillness, the purity of light, and the dew-sweet bird-song rising in the street again.

In all these ancient, ever-new, unchanging, always magic acts of life and light and morning one felt the huge impending presence of the war. And one felt it in the brooding hush of noon, in the ring of the ice-tongs in the street, the cool whine of the ice-saws droning through the smoking block, in leaf, and blade and flower, in smell of tar, and the sudden haunting green-gold summer absence of a street-car after it had gone.

The war had got in everything: it was in things that moved, and in things that were still, in the animate red silence of an old brick wall as well as in all the thronging life and traffic of the streets. It was in the faces of the people passing, and in ten thousand familiar moments of man's daily life and business.

And lonely, wild, and haunting, calling us on forever with the winding of its far lost horn, it had got into the time-enchanted loneliness of the magic hills around us, in all the sudden, wild and lonely lights that came and passed and vanished on the massed green of the wilderness.

The war was in far cries and broken sounds and cow-bells tinkling in the gusty wind, and in the far, wild, wailing joy and sorrow of a departing train, as it rushed eastward, seaward, war-ward through a valley of the South in the green spell and golden magic of full June, and in the houses where men lived, the brief flame and fire of sheeted window panes.

And it was in field and gulch and hollow, in the sweet green mountain valleys fading into dusk, and in the hill-flanks reddened with the ancient light, and slanting fast into steep cool shade and lilac silence. It was in the whole huge mystery of earth that, after all the dusty tumult of the day, could lapse with such immortal stillness to the hush, the joy, the sorrow of oncoming night.

The war had got into all sounds and secrecies, the sorrow, longing, and delight, the mystery, hunger and wild joy that came from the deep-breasted heart of fragrant, all-engulfing night. It was in the sweet and secret rustling of the leaves in summer streets, in footsteps coming quiet, slow, and lonely along the darkness of a leafy street, in screen doors slammed, and silence, the distant barking of a dog, far voices, laughter, faint pulsing music at a dance, and in all the casual voices of the night, far, strangely near, most intimate and familiar.

And suddenly, as I sat there under the proud and secret mystery of huge-starred, velvet-breasted night, hearing my father's great voice sounding from the porch again, the war, with a wild and intolerable loneliness of ecstasy and desire came to me in the sudden throbbing of a racing motor,

The Old Kentucky Home boardinghouse.
Courtesy of the North Carolina Division of Archives and History, Raleigh

far-away silence, an image of the cool sweet darkness of the mountainside, the white flesh and yielding tenderness of women. And even as I thought of this I heard the rich, sensual welling of a woman's voice, voluptuous, low, and tender, from the darkness of a summer porch across the street.

What had the war changed? What had it done to us? What miracle of transformation had it wrought upon our lives? It had changed nothing; it had heightened, intensified, and made glorious all the ancient and familiar things of life. It had added hope to hope, joy to joy, and life to life; and from that vital wizardry it had rescued all our lives from hopelessness and despair, and made us live again who thought that we were lost.

The war seemed to have collected in a single image of joy, and power, and proud compacted might all of the thousand images of joy and power and all-exulting life which we had always had, and for which we had never had a word before. Over the fields of silent and mysterious night it seemed that we could hear the nation marching, that we could hear, soft and thunderous in the night, the million-footed unison of marching men. And that single glorious image of all-collected joy and unity and might had given new life and new hope to all of us.

My father was old, he was sick with a cancer that flowered and fed forever at his entrails, eating from day to day the gaunt sinew of his life away beyond a hope or remedy, and we knew that he was dying. Yet, under the magic life and hope the war had brought to us, his life seemed to have revived again out of its grief of pain, its death of joy, its sorrow of irrevocable memory.

For a moment he seemed to live again in his full prime. And instantly we were all released from the black horror of death and time that hung above him, from the nightmare terror that had menaced us for years. Instantly we were freed from the evil spell of sorrowful time and memory that had made his living death more horrible than his real one could ever be.

And instantly the good life, the golden and jubilant life of childhood, in whose full magic we had been sustained by the power of his life, and which had seemed so lost and irrevocable that it had a dreamlike strangeness when we thought of it, had, under this sudden flare of life and joy and war, returned in all its various and triumphant colors. And for a moment we believed that all would be again for us as it had been, that he never could grow old and die, but that he must live forever, and that the summertime, the orchard and bright morning, would be ours again, could never die.

I could hear him talking now about old wars and ancient troubles, hurling against the present and its leaders the full indictment of his soaring rhetoric that howled, rose, fell, and swept out into the night, piercing all quarters of the darkness with the naked penetration which his voice had in the old days when he sat talking on his porch in summer darkness, and the neighborhood attended and was still.

Now as my father talked, I could hear the boarders on the porch attending in the same way, the stealthy creak of a rocker now and then, a low word spoken, a question, protest or agreement, and then their hungry, feeding, and attentive silence as my father talked. He spoke of all the wars and troubles he had known, told how he had stood, "a bare-foot country boy," beside a dusty road twelve miles from Gettysburg, and had watched the ragged rebels march past upon the road that led to death and battle and the shipwreck of their hopes.

He spoke of the faint and ominous trembling of the guns across the hot brooding silence of the countryside, and how silence, wonder, and unspoken questions filled the hearts of all the people, and how they had gone about their work upon the farm as usual. He spoke of the years that had followed on the war when he was a stone-cutter's apprentice in Baltimore, and he spoke of ancient joys and labors, forgotten acts and histories, and he spoke then with familiar memory of the lost Americans—the strange, lost, time-far, dead Americans, the remote, voiceless, and bewhiskered faces of the great Americans, who were more lost to me than Egypt, more far from me than the Tartarian coasts, more haunting strange than Cipango or the lost faces of the first dynastic kings that built the Pyramids—and whom he had seen, heard, known, found familiar in the full pulse, and passion, and proud glory of his youth: the lost, time-far, voiceless faces of Buchanan, Johnson, Douglas, Blaine—the proud, vacant, time-strange and bewhiskered visages of Garfield, Arthur, Harrison, and Hayes.

"Ah, Lord!" he said—his voice rang out in darkness like a gong, "Ah, Lord!—I've known all of 'em since James Buchanan's time—for I was a boy of six when he took office!" Here he paused a moment, lunged forward violently in his rocking chair, and spat cleanly out a spurt of strong tobacco juice across the porch-rail into the loamy earth, the night-sweet fragrance of the geranium beds. "Yes, sir," he said gravely, lunging back again, while the attentive, hungry boarders waited in the living darkness and were still, "I remember all of them since James Buchanan's time, and I've seen most of them that came since Lincoln!—Ah, Lord!" he paused briefly for another waiting moment, shaking his grave head sadly in the dark. "Well do I remember the day when I stood on a street in Baltimore— poor friendless orphan that I was!" my father went on sorrowfully, but somewhat illogically, since at this time his mother was alive and in good health, upon her little farm in Pennsylvania, and would continue so for almost fifty years—"a poor friendless country boy of sixteen years, alone in the great city where I had come to learn my trade as an apprentice—and heard Andrew Johnson, then the President of this *great* nation," said my father, "speak from the platform of a horse-car—and he was so drunk—so *drunk*—" he howled, "the President of this country was so *drunk* that they had to stand on each side of him, and hold him as he spoke—or he'd

FALL PUBLICATIONS

STORIES
by Thomas Wolfe,
author of "Look Homeward, Angel," and "Of Time and the River"

Publication Date, October $2.50

The Author: *Mr. Wolfe has been called a man of authentic genius by leading critics. This book will support their judgment.*

The Book: Two of the stories are short novels—completely objective studies of women. One, "The Web of Earth," runs to 30,000 words, and "A Woman's Life" to 25,000 words. In these two stories the complete beings of one old woman and a young woman are completely unfolded with consummate skill.

Among the other stories are "The Men of Old Catawba" (full of earthy humor, a genuine American piece), "One of the Girls in Our Party" (an affectionate satire on the Middle Western school teacher), "The Four Lost Men" (which is based on a memory), "Circus at Dawn," "Dark in the Forest, Strange as Time," "Gulliver" (which shows how the world looks to a man of six feet six), and a number of others.

One would not think that after two vast novels new aspects of Wolfe's talent could be revealed—but they truly are. His humor, in particular, comes into full and brilliant play.

The Market: *Readers of "Of Time and the River," and every one interested in good fiction.*

The Scribner's Fall 1935 catalogue entry for the still-untitled *From Death to Morning*. In response to critic Burton Rascoe's assertion that Wolfe's fiction was humorless, the text emphasized the stories' comic elements.
Collection of the editors

a-gone head over heels into the gutter!" Here he paused, wet his great thumb briefly, cleared his throat with considerable satisfaction, lunged forward violently again in his rocking chair and spat strongly a wad of bright tobacco juice into the loamy fragrance of the dark geranium bed.

"The first vote I ever cast for President," my father continued presently, as he lunged back again, "I cast in 1872, in Baltimore, for that *great* man—that brave and noble soldier—U. S. Grant! And I have voted for every Republican nominee for President ever since. I voted for Rutherford Hayes of Ohio in 1876—that was the year, as you well know, of the great Hayes-Tilden controversy, in 1880 for James Abram Garfield—that *great* good man," he said passionately, "who was so foully and brutally done to death by the cowardly assault of a murderous assassin." He paused, wet his thumb, breathing heavily, lunged forward in his rocking chair, and spat again. "In 1884, I cast my vote for James G. Blaine in the year that Grover Cleveland defeated him," he said shortly, "for Benjamin Harrison in 1888, and for Harrison again in 1892, the time that Cleveland got in for his second term—a time we will all remember to our dying days," my father said grimly, "for the Democrats were in and we had soup kitchens. And, you can mark my words," he howled, "you'll have them again, before these next four years are over—your guts will grease your backbone, as sure as there's a God in heaven, before that fearful, that awful, that cruel, inhuman and bloodthirsty Monster who kept us out of war," my father jeered derisively, "is done with you—for hell, ruin, misery, and damnation commence every time the Democrats get in. You can rest assured of that!" he said shortly, cleared his throat, wet his thumb, lunged forward violently and spat again. And for a moment there was silence and the boarders waited.

"Ah, Lord!" my father said at length sadly, gravely, in a low, almost inaudible tone. And suddenly, all the old life and howling fury of his rhetoric had gone from him: he was an old man again, sick, indifferent, dying, and his voice had grown old, worn, weary, sad.

"Ah, Lord!" he muttered, shaking his head sadly, thinly, wearily in the dark. "I've seen them all. . . . I've seen them come and go . . . Garfield, Arthur, Harrison, and Hayes . . . and all . . . all . . . all of them are dead. . . . I'm the only one that's left," he said illogically, "and soon I'll be gone, too." And for a moment he was silent. "It's pretty strange when you come to think of it," he muttered. "By God it is!" And he was silent, and darkness, mystery, and night were all about us.

Garfield, Arthur, Harrison, and Hayes—time of my father's time, blood of his blood, life of his life, had been living, real, and actual people in all the passion, power, and feeling of my father's youth. And for me they were the lost Americans: their gravely vacant and bewhiskered faces mixed, melted, swam together in the sea-depths of a past intangible, immeasurable, and unknowable as the buried city of Persepolis.

And they were lost.

For who was Garfield, martyred man, and who had seen him in the streets of life? Who could believe his footfalls ever sounded on a lonely pavement? Who had heard the casual and familiar tones of Chester Arthur? And where was Harrison? Where was Hayes? Which had the whiskers, which the burnsides: which was which?

Were they not lost?

Into their ears, as ours, the tumults of forgotten crowds, upon their brains the million printings of lost time, and suddenly upon their dying sight the brief bitter pain and joy of a few death-bright, fixed and fading memories: the twisting of a leaf upon a bough, the grinding felloe-rim against the curb, the long, distant and retreating thunder of a train upon the rails.

Garfield, Hayes, and Harrison were Ohio men; but only the name of Garfield had been brightened by his blood. But at night had they not heard the howlings of demented wind, the sharp, clean, windy raining to the earth of acorns? Had all of them not walked down lonely roads at night in winter and seen a light and known it was theirs? Had all of them not known the wilderness?

Had they not known the smell of old bound calf and well-worn leathers, the Yankee lawyer's smell of strong tobacco spit and courthouse urinals, the smell of horses, harness, hay, and sweating country men, of jury rooms and court rooms—the strong male smell of Justice at the county seat, and heard a tap along dark corridors where fell a drop in darkness with a punctual crescent monotone of time, dark time?

Had not Garfield, Hayes, and Harrison studied law in offices with a dark brown smell? Had not the horses trotted past below their windows in wreaths of dust along a straggling street of shacks and buildings with false fronts? Had they not heard below them the voices of men talking, loitering up in drawling heat? Had they not heard the casual, rich-fibered, faintly howling country voices, and heard the rustling of a woman's skirt, and waiting silence, slyly lowered tones of bawdry and then huge guffaws, slapped meaty thighs, and high fat choking laughter? And in the dusty dozing heat, while time buzzed slowly, like a fly, had not Garfield, Arthur, Harrison, and Hayes then smelled the river, the humid, subtly fresh, half-rotten river, and thought of the white flesh of the women then beside the river, and felt a slow impending passion in their entrails, a heavy rending power in their hands?

Then Garfield, Arthur, Harrison, and Hayes had gone to war, and each became a brigadier or major-general. All were bearded men: they saw a spattering of bright blood upon the leaves, and they heard the soldiers talking in the dark of food and women. They held the bridge-head in bright dust at places with such names as Wilson's Mill and Spangler's Run, and their men smashed cautiously through dense undergrowth. And they had heard the surgeons cursing after battles, and the little rasp of saws. They had seen boys standing awkwardly holding their entrails in their hands, and pleading pitifully with fear-bright eyes: "Is it bad, General? Do you think it's bad?"

When the canister came through it made a ragged hole. It smashed through tangled leaves and boughs, sometimes it plunked solidly into the fiber of a tree. Sometimes when it struck a man it tore away the roof of his brain, the wall of his skull, raggedly, so that his brains seethed out upon a foot of wilderness, and the blood blackened and congealed, and he lay there in his thick clumsy uniform, with a smell of urine in the wool, in the casual, awkward, and incompleted attitude of sudden death. And when Garfield, Arthur, Harrison, and Hayes saw these things they saw that it was not like the picture they had had, as children, it was not like the works of Walter Scott and William Gillmore Sims. They saw that the hole was not clean and small and in the central front, and the field was not green nor fenced, nor mown. Over the vast and immemorable earth the quivering heated light of afternoon was shining, a field swept rudely upward to a lift of rugged wood, and field by field, gulley by gulch by fold, the earth advanced in rude, sweet, limitless convolutions.

Then Garfield, Arthur, Harrison, and Hayes had paused by the bridge-head for a moment and were still, seeing the bright blood at noon upon the trampled wheat, feeling the brooding hush of six o'clock across the fields where all the storming feet had passed at dawn, seeing the way the rough field hedge leaned out across the dusty road, the casual intrusions of the coarse field grasses and the hot dry daisies to the edges of the road, seeing the rock-bright shallows of the creek, the sweet cool shade and lean of the river trees across the water.

They paused then by the bridge-head looking at the water. They saw the stark blank flatness of the old red mill that somehow was like sunset, coolness, sorrow, and delight, and looking at the faces of the dead boys among the wheat, the most-oh-most familiar-plain, the death-strange faces of the dead Americans, they stood there for a moment, thinking, feeling, thinking, with strong, wordless wonder in their hearts:

"As we leaned on the sills of evening, as we stood in the frames of the marvellous doors, as we were received into silence, the flanks of the slope and the slanted light, as we saw the strange hushed shapes upon the land, the muted distances, knowing all things then—what could we say except that all our comrades were spread quietly around us and that noon was far?*

"What can we say now of the lonely land—what can we say now of the deathless shapes and substances—what can we say who have lived here with our lives, bone, blood, and brain, and all our tongueless languages, hearing on many a casual road the plain-familiar voices of Americans, and who to-morrow will be buried in the earth, knowing the fields will steep to silence after us, the slant light deepen on the slopes, and peace and evening will come back again—at one now with the million shapes and single substance of our land, at one with evening, peace, the huge stride of the undulant oncoming night, at one, also, with morning?

"Silence receive us, and the field of peace, hush of the measureless land, the unabated distances; shape of the one and single substance and the million forms, replenish us, restore us, and unite us with your vast images of quietness and joy. Stride of the undulant night, come swiftly now; engulf us, silence, in your great-starred secrecy; speak to our hearts of stillness, for we have, save this, no speech.

"There is the bridge we crossed, the mill we slept in, and the creek. There is a field of wheat, a hedge, a dusty road, an apple orchard, and the sweet wild tangle of a wood upon that hill. And there is six o'clock across the fields again, now and always, as it was and will be to world's end forever. And some of us have died this morning coming through the field—and that was time—time—time. We shall not come again, we never shall come back again, we never shall come back along this road again as we did once at morning—so, brothers, let us look again before we go. . . . There is the mill, and there the hedge, and there the shallows of

*This paragraph and the two paragraphs following are not in the long typescript.

FROM DEATH TO MORNING

These stories reveal in Mr. Wolfe qualities as a writer unsuspected by the thousands who have read his longer works. They show what perfection he can achieve within a restricted compass — especially noticeable in some of the five and six page stories here included, which for economy and precision of style are unsurpassed. Here Mr. Wolfe recreates a world as perfectly as on the vast canvas of his novels. For all its varying moods of humor or profound perception, "From Death to Morning" has a unity and a progress, as suggested in the title, which raise it far above the average story collection.

FROM DEATH TO MORNING

stories by THOMAS WOLFE

SCRIBNERS

THOMAS WOLFE

"A triumphant demonstration that Thomas Wolfe has the stamina to produce a magnificent epic of American life." Peter Monro Jack in The N.Y. Times

Of Time and the River
By
Thomas Wolfe
author of "From Death to Morning" and "Look Homeward, Angel"

•

"The least that can be said about Thomas Wolfe is that he is one of the most extraordinary phenomena in modern literature and of his novel that the reading of it must surely be an unforgettable experience. ... Mr. Wolfe is genuinely extending the boundaries of the novel."
London Times Literary Supplement

"He has more material, more vitality, more originality, more gusto than any two contemporary British novelists put together... And he entirely escapes the sordid, whining defeatism of so many of his American contemporaries."
Henry Seidel Canby in The Saturday Review

"The story of the novels, sensations and ideas of Eugene Gant is told in such glowing prose that one reads for the very joy of reading... Thomas Wolfe is a phenomenon out of step with his generation, which is crawling on its bellies. Once one seizes and apprehends the scale on which he writes, his book becomes an adventure not to be missed."
Harry Hansen in Harper's Magazine

"We have a voice in this novel which sounds as if it were from demons, gods and seraphim — in chorus — and, strangely, a voice speaking of intimate and common things... A hundred stories and five years of life, richly experienced, deeply felt, minutely and lyrically recorded."
Burton Rascoe in The N.Y. Herald Tribune

CHARLES SCRIBNER'S SONS, NEW YORK

Thomas Wolfe

"The most prodigious book of 1935 was 'Of Time and the River' by Thomas Wolfe, who can best be characterized by being called the Walt Whitman of novelists, impassioned and magnificent." — Carl Van Doren in The N.Y. Herald Tribune

Dust jacket for the 1935 first printing.
Collection of the editors

the rock-bright waters of the creek, and there the sweet and most familiar coolness of the trees—and surely we have been this way before!" they cried.

"Oh, surely, brothers, we have sat upon the bridge, before the mill, and sung together by the rock-bright waters of the creek at evening, and come across the wheatfield in the morning and heard the dew-sweet bird-song rising from the hedge before! You plain, oh-most-familiar and most homely earth, proud earth of this huge land unutterable, proud nobly swelling earth, in all your delicacy, wildness, savagery, and terror—grand earth in all your loneliness, beauty and wild joy, terrific earth in all your limitless fecundities, swelling with infinite fold and convolution into the reaches of the West forever—American earth!—bridge, hedge, and creek and dusty road—you plain tremendous poetry of Wilson's Mill, where boys died in the wheat this morning—you unutterable far-near, strange-familiar, homely earth of magic, for which a word would do if we could find it, for which a word would do if we could call it by its name, for which a word would do that never can be spoken, that can never be forgotten, and that will never be revealed—oh, proud, familiar, nobly swelling earth, it seems we must have known you before! It seems we must have known you forever, but all we know for certain is that we came along this road one time at morning, and now our blood is painted on the wheat, and you are ours now, we are yours forever—and there is something here we never shall remember—there is something here we never shall forget!"

Had Garfield, Arthur, Harrison, and Hayes been young? Or had they all been born with flowing whiskers, sideburns, and wing collars, speaking gravely from the cradle of their mother's arms the noble vacant sonorities of far-seeing statesmanship? It could not be. Had they not all been young men in the 'Thirties, the 'Forties, and the 'Fifties? Did they not, as we, cry out at night along deserted roads into demented winds? Did they not, as we, cry out in ecstasy and exultancy, as the full measure of their hunger, their potent and inchoate hope, went out into that single wordless cry?

Did they not, as we, when young, prowl softly up and down in the dark hours of the night, seeing the gas-lamps flare and flutter on the corner, falling with livid light upon the corners of old cobbled streets of brown-stone houses? Had they not heard the lonely rhythmic clopping of a horse, the jounting wheels of a hansom cab, upon those barren cobbles? And had they not waited, trembling in the darkness till the horse and cab had passed, had vanished with the lonely recession of shod hoofs, and then were heard no more?

And then had Garfield, Arthur, Harrison, and Hayes not waited, waited in the silence of the night, prowling up and down the lonely cobbled street, with trembling lips, numb entrails, pounding hearts? Had they not set their jaws, made sudden indecisive movements, felt terror, joy, a numb impending ecstasy, and waited, waited then—for what? Had they not waited, hearing sounds of shifting engines in the yards at night, hearing the hoarse, gaseous breaths of little engines through the grimy fan-flare of their funnels? Had they not waited there in that dark street with the fierce lone hunger of a boy, feeling around them the immense and moving quietness of sleep, the heartbeats of ten thousand sleeping men, as they waited, waited in the night?

Had they not, as we, then turned their eyes up and seen the huge starred visage of the night, the immense and lilac darkness of America in April? Had they not heard the sudden, shrill, and piping whistle of a departing engine? Had they not waited, thinking, feeling, seeing then the immense mysterious continent of night, the wild and lyric earth, so casual, sweet, and strange-familiar, in all its space and savagery and terror, its mystery and joy, its limitless sweep and rudeness, its delicate and savage fecundity? Had they not had a vision of the plains, the mountains, and the rivers flowing in the darkness, the huge pattern of the everlasting earth and the all-engulfing wilderness of America?

Had they not felt, as we have felt, as they waited in the night, the huge, lonely earth of night-time and America, on which ten thousand lonely sleeping little towns were strewn? Had they not seen the fragile network of light, racketing, ill-joined little rails across the land, over which the lonely little trains rushed on in darkness, flinging a handful of lost echoes at the river's edge, leaving an echo in the cut's resounding cliff, and being engulfed then in huge lonely night, in all-brooding, all-engulfing night? Had they not know, as we have known, the wild secret joy and mystery of the everlasting earth, the lilac dark, the savage, silent, all-possessing wilderness that gathered in around ten thousand lonely little towns, ten million lost and lonely sleepers, and waited, and abode forever, and was still?

Had not Garfield, Arthur, Harrison, and Hayes then waited, feeling wild joy and sorrow in their hearts, and a savage hunger and desire—a flame, a fire, a fury—burning fierce and lean and lonely in the night, burning forever while the sleepers slept? Were they not burning, burning, burning, even as the rest of us have burned? Were Garfield, Arthur, Harrison, and Hayes not burning in the night? Were they not burning forever in the silence of the little towns, with all the fierce hunger, savage passion, limitless desire that young men in this land have known in the darkness?

Had Garfield, Arthur, Harrison, and Hayes not waited then, as we have waited, with numb lips and pounding hearts and fear, delight, strong joy and terror stirring in their entrails as they stood in the silent street before a house, proud, evil, lighted—certain, secret, and alone? And as they heard the hoof, the wheel, the sudden whistle and the immense and sleeping silence of the town, did they not wait there in the darkness, thinking:

"Oh, there are new lands, morning, and a shining city. Soon, soon, soon!"

Did not Garfield, Arthur, Harrison, and Hayes, those fierce and jubilant young men, who waited there, as we have waited, in the silent barren street, with trembling lips, numb hands, with terror, savage joy, fierce rapture alive and stirring in their entrails—did they not feel, as we have felt, when they heard the shrill departing warning of the whistle in the dark, the sound of great wheels pounding at the river's edge? Did they not feel, as we have felt, as they waited there in the intolerable sweetness, wildness, mystery, and terror of the great earth in the month of April, and knew themselves alone, alive and young and mad and secret with desire and hunger in the great sleep-silence of the night, the impending, cruel, all-promise of this land? Were they not torn, as we have been, by sharp pain and wordless lust, the asp of time, the thorn of spring, the sharp, the tongueless cry? Did they not say:

"Oh, there are women in the East—and new lands, morning, and a shining city! There are forgotten fume-flaws of bright smoke above Manhattan, the forest of masts about the crowded isle, the proud cleavages of departing ships, the soaring web, the wing-like swoop and joy of the great bridge, and men with derby hats who come across the Bridge to greet us—come, brothers, let us go to find them all! For the huge murmur of the city's million-footed life, far, bee-like, drowsy, strange as time, has come to haunt our ears with all its golden prophecy of joy and triumph, fortune, happiness, and love such as no men before have ever known. Oh, brothers, in the city, in the far-shining glorious time-enchanted spell of that enfabled city we shall find great men and lovely women, and unceasingly ten thousand new delights, a thousand magical adventures! We shall wake at morning in our rooms of lavish brown to hear the hoof and wheel upon the city street again, and smell the harbor, fresh, half-rotten, with its bracelet of bright tides, its traffic of proud sea-borne ships, its purity and joy of dancing morning-gold.

"Street of the day, with the unceasing promise of your million-footed life, we come to you!" they cried. "Street of the thunderous wheels at noon, street of the great parades of marching men, the band's bright on-coming blare, the brave stick-candy whippings of a flag, street of the cries and shouts, the swarming feet,—street of the jounting cabs, the ringing hooves, the horse-cars and the jingling bells, the in-horse ever bending its sad nodding head toward its lean and patient comrade on the right—great street of furious life and movement, noon, and joyful labors, your image blazes in our hearts forever, and we come!

"Street of the morning, street of hope!" they cried. "Street of coolness, slanted light, the frontal cliff and gulch of steep blue shade, street of the dancing morning-gold of waters on the flashing tides, street of the rusty weathered slips, the blunt-nosed ferry foaming in with its packed wall of small white staring faces, all silent and intent, all turned toward *you* — proud street! Street of the pungent sultry smells of new-ground coffee, the good green smell of money, the fresh half-rotten harbor smells with all its evocation of your mast-bound harbor and its tide of ships, great street!— Street of the old buildings grimed richly with the warm and mellow dingi-ness of trade—street of the million morning feet forever hurrying onward in the same direction—proud street of hope and joy and morning, in your steep canyon we shall win the wealth, the fame, the power and the esteem which our lives and talents merit!

"Street of the night!" they cried, "great street of mystery and suspense, terror and delight, eagerness and hope, street edged forever with the dark menace of impending joy, an unknown happiness and fulfilment, street of gaiety, warmth, and evil, street of the great hotels, the lavish bars and restaurants, and the softly golden glow, the fading lights and empetalled whiteness of a thousand hushed white thirsty faces in the crowded thea-tres, street of the tidal flood of faces, lighted with your million lights and all thronging, tireless and unquenched in their insatiate searching after pleasure, street of the lovers coming along with slow steps, their faces turned toward each other, lost in the oblivion of love among the everlast-ing web and weaving of the crowd, street of the white face, the painted mouth, the shining and inviting eye—oh, street of night, with all your mystery, joy, and terror—we have thought of you, proud street.

"And we shall move at evening in the noiseless depths of sumptuous carpets through all the gaiety, warmth, and brilliant happiness of great lighted chambers of the night, filled with the mellow thrum and languor of the violins, and where the loveliest and most desirable women in the world—the beloved daughters of great merchants, bankers, millionaires, or rich young widows, beautiful, loving, and alone—are moving with a slow proud undulance, a look of depthless tenderness in their fragile, lovely faces. And the loveliest of them all," they cried, "is ours, is ours forever, if we want her! For, brothers, in the city, in the far-shining, magic, golden city, we shall move among great men and glorious women and know nothing but strong joy and happiness forever, winning by our courage, talent, and deserving the highest and most honored place in the most fortunate and happy life that men have known, if only we will go and make it ours!"

So thinking, feeling, waiting as we have waited in the sleeping silence of the night in silent streets, hearing, as we have heard, the sharp blast of the warning whistle, the thunder of great wheels upon the river's edge, feeling, as we have felt, the mystery of night-time and of April, the huge impending presence, the wild and secret promise, of the savage, lonely, everlasting earth, finding, as we have found, no doors to enter, and being torn, as we were torn, by the thorn of spring, the sharp, the wordless cry, did they not carry—these young men of the past, Garfield, Arthur, Harrison, and Hayes—even as we have carried, within their little tenements of bone, blood, sinew, sweat, and agony, the intolerable burden of all the pain, joy, hope and savage hunger that a man can suffer, that the world can know?

Were they not lost? Were they not lost, as all of us have been who have known youth and hunger in this land, and who have waited lean and mad and lonely in the night, and who have found no goal, no wall, no dwelling, and no door?

The years flow by like water, and one day it is spring again. Shall we ever ride out of the gates of the East again, as we did once at morning, and seek again, as we did then, new lands, the promise of the war, and glory, joy, and triumph, and a shining city?

O youth, still wounded, living, feeling with a woe unutterable, still grieving with a grief intolerable, still thirsting with a thirst unquenchable— where are we to seek? For the wild tempest breaks above us, the wild fury beats about us, the wild hunger feeds upon us—and we are houseless, doorless, unassuaged, and driven on forever; and our brains are mad, our hearts are wild and wordless, and we cannot speak.

The Four Lost Men

Substantive Variants between
Previously Published Versions

Scribner's magazine (February 1934), 101–8 [*From Death to Morning* version, 71–86 in this volume.

101.I.9	savage goat-cry of their [71.6–7 savage cry of all their
101.I.33–35	noon, in the warm dusty stir and flutter and the feathery clucking of the sun-warm hens at noon. One felt it in the ring [72.3 noon, in the ring
101.I.37–101.II.7	block. One felt it poignantly somehow, in the solid lonely liquid leather shuffle of men in shirt-sleeves coming home to lunch in one direction in the brooding hush and time-enchanted spell of noon, and in screens that slammed and sudden silence. And one felt it in the humid warmth and hungry fragrance of the cooking turnip greens, in leaf [72.5 block, in leaf
101.II.10–12	¶ In all these ancient, most familiar things and acts and colors of our lives, one felt, with numbing ecstasy, the impending presence of the war. The war [72.7 ¶ The war
101.II.30–32	June. The war was in the ancient red-gold light of fading day, that fell without violence or heat upon the streets of life, the houses [72.19 June, and in the houses
102.I.1–4	whole earth breathing the last heat and weariness of day out in the huge hush and joy and sorrow [72.24–25 whole huge mystery of earth that, after

all the dusty tumult of the day, could lapse with such immortal stillness to the hush, the joy, the sorrow

102.I.4 ¶ Finally, the war [72.27 ¶ The war

102.I.14–15 familiar, remote as time, as haunting as the briefness of our days. [72.34 familiar.

102.I.24 the low, rich [73.3 the rich

103.I.2–3 Hayes. ¶ "Ah [75.17–18 Hayes. [space break] ¶ "Ah

104.II.34 rock-bright sallows of [80.1 rock-bright shallows of

105.I.1 and tomorrow [80.18 and who to-morrow

105.II.21–22 out the fierce goat-cry of ecstacy [82.29 out in ecstasy

105.II.44–45 funnels, the racketing clack of wheels upon the light, ill-laid, ill-joined rails? Had [83.8 funnels? Had

106.I.4 waited, waited, waited [83.10–11 waited, waited

106.I.24 of the light [83.24–25 of light

106.I.36–37 waited, feeling the goat-cry swelling in their throats, feeling wild [83.33–34 waited, feeling wild

106.I.46–II.10 darkness? ¶ Were they not burning with the wild and wordless hope, the incredible belief that all young men have known before the promise of that huge mirage, the deathless dupe and invincible illusion of this savage all-exultant land where all things are impending and where young men starve? Were they not burning in the enfabled magic, mystery, and joy of lilac dark, the lonely, savage, secret, everlasting earth on which we lived, and wrought, and perished, mad with hunger, unfed, famished, furious, unassuaged? Were they not burning, burning where a million doors of glory, love, unutterable fulfilment, impended, waited in the dark for us, were here, were here around us in the dark forever, were here beside us in the dark forever, were ready to our touch forever, and that duped us, mocked forever at our hunger, maddened our hearts and brains with searching, took our youth, our strength, our love, our life, and killed us, and were never found? ¶ Had [84.1–2 darkness? ¶ Had

106.II.13 they waited in [84.4 they stood in

106.II.17–19 town, the lonely, wild and secret earth, the lilac dark, the huge starred visage of the night—did [84.7 town, did

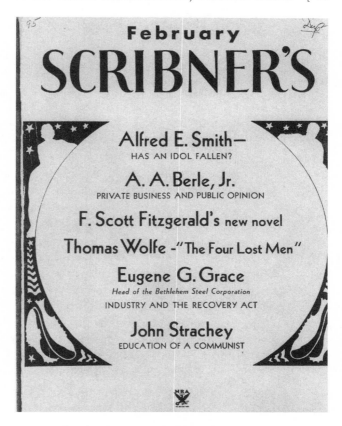

The short version of "The Four Lost Men"
was published in February 1934.
Collection of the editors

106.II.21–107.I.51 soon!" ¶ And then as Garfield, Arthur, Harrison, and
Hayes prowled softly up and down in the dark cob-
bled streets, hearing the sudden shrill departure of
the whistle in the night, the great wheels pounding
at the river's edge, feeling the lilac dark, the heartbeats of the sleeping men, and the attentive silence,
the terror, savagery, and joy, the huge mystery and
promise of the immense and silent earth, thinking,
feeling, thinking, with wild, silent joy, intolerable
desire, did they not say: ¶ "Oh, there are women in
the West and we shall find them. They will be waiting for us, calm, tranquil, corn-haired, unsurprised,

looking across the wall of level grain with level eyes, looking into the flaming domains of the red, the setting sun, at the great wall and the soaring vistas of the western ranges. Oh, there are lavish, corn-haired women in the West with tranquil eyes," cried Garfield, Arthur, Harrison, and Hayes, "and we shall find them waiting in their doors for us at evening!" ¶ "And there are women in the South," they said, "with dark eyes and the white magnolia faces. They are moving beneath the droop of tree-barred levels of the South. Now they are moving on the sweep of ancient lawns, beside the great slow-flowing rivers in the night! Their step is light and soundless as the dark, they drift the white ghost-glimmer of their beauty under ancient trees, their words are soft and slow and hushed, and sweeter far than honey, and suddenly their low and tender laugh, slow, rich, and sensual, comes welling from the great vat of the dark. The perfume of their slow white flesh is flower-sweet, magnolia strange, and filled with all the secret languors of desire! Oh, there are secret women in the South," they cried, "who move by darkness under drooping trees in the white ghost-glimmer of magnolia loveliness, and we shall find them!" ¶ "And there are women in the North," cried Garfield, Arthur, Harrison, and Hayes, "who wait for us with Viking eyes, the deep breast and the great limbs of the Amazons. There are powerful and lovely women in the North," they said, "whose eyes are blue and depthless as a mountain lake. Their glorious hair is braided into ropes of ripened grain, and their names are Lundquist, Neilsen, Svensen, Jorgenson, and Brandt. They are waiting for us in the wheat-fields of the North, they are waiting for us at the edges of the plains, they are waiting for us in the forests of great trees. Their eyes are true and level, and their great hearts are the purest and most faithful on the earth, and they will wait for us until we come to them. ¶ "There are ten thousand lonely little towns at night," cried Garfield, Arthur, Harrison, and Hayes, "ten thousand lonely little towns of sleeping men, and

we shall come to them forever in the night. We shall
come to them like storm and fury, with a demonic
impulse of wild joy, dark chance, dropping suddenly
upon them from the fast express at night—leaving
the train in darkness, in the dark mid-watches of the
night, and being left then to the sudden silence, mystery, and promise of an unknown little town. Oh, we
shall come to them forever in the night," they cried,
"in winter among howling winds and swirling snow.
Then we shall make our tracks along the sheeted
fleecy whiteness of an empty silent little street, and
find our door at length, and know the instant that
we come to it that it is ours. ¶ "Coming by storm
and darkness to the lonely, chance and secret towns,"
they said, "we shall find the well-loved face, the
longed-for step, the well-known voice, there in the
darkness while storm beats about the house and the
white mounting drifts of swirling snow engulf us.
Then we shall know the flower-whiteness of a face
below us, the night-time darkness of a cloud of hair
across our arm, and know all the mystery, tenderness,
and surrender, of a white-dark beauty, the fragrant
whiteness, the slow bounty of a velvet undulance,
the earth-deep fruitfulness of love. And we shall stay
there while storm howls about the house," they said,
"and huge drifts rise about us. We shall leave forever
in the whitened silence of the morning, and always
know the chance, the secret and the well-beloved will
be there waiting for us when storms howl at night,
and we come again through swirling snow, leaving
our footprints on the whitened, empty, silent streets
of unknown little towns, lost at the heart of storm
and darkness upon the lonely, wild, all-secret mystery
of the earth." ¶ And finally did not [84.9–10 soon!"
¶ Did not

107.II.5   in all the [84.16 in the
107.II.34–108.I.10   morning-gold—and feel, with an unspeakable sorrow and delight, that there are ships there, there are
ships—and something in our hearts we cannot utter.
¶ "And we shall smell the excellent sultry fragrance
of boiling coffee, and think of silken luxury of great

walnut chambers in whose shuttered amber morning-
light proud beauties slowly stir in sensual warmth
their lavish limbs. Then we shall smell, with the
sharp relish of young hunger, the grand breakfast
smells: the pungent bacon, crisping to a turn, the
grilled kidneys, eggs, and sausages, and the fragrant
stacks of gold-brown wheat cakes smoking hot. And
we shall move, alive and strong and full of hope,
through all the swarming lanes of morning and know
the good green smell of money, the heavy leathers
and the walnut of great merchants, the power, the
joy, the certitude and ease of proud success. ¶ "We
shall come at furious noon to slake our thirst with
drinks of rare and subtle potency in sumptuous bars
of swart mahogany in the good fellowship of men,
the spicy fragrance of the lemon rind and angostura
bitters. Then, hunger whetted, pulse aglow and leaping with the sharp spur of our awakened appetite, we
shall eat from the snowy linen of the greatest restaurants in the world. We shall be suavely served and
tenderly cared for by the pious unction of devoted
waiters. We shall be quenched with old wine and fed
with the rare and priceless honesty, the maddening
succulence of grand familiar food and noble cooking, fit to match the peerless relish of our hunger!" ¶
"Street [84.38–85.1 morning-gold. ¶ "Street

108.I.11–12 cried. "Streets of [85.2 cried. "Street of
108.I.12 noon, streets of [85.3 noon, street of
108.I.15–17 feet, the man-swarm ever passing in its million-
footed weft—street [85.5 feet,—street